Medicine Makers of Kalamazoo

Medicine Makers
of Kalamazoo

LEONARD ENGEL

McGRAW-HILL BOOK COMPANY, INC.

New York   Toronto   London   1961

MEDICINE MAKERS OF KALAMAZOO

Preface

The question may be asked, Why should one write a history of a pharmaceutical company? The answer is simple. The pharmaceutical industry has played a prominent role in the sweeping advances that have so transformed medicine in the past twenty-five years. In the process, the industry has inevitably attracted to itself a great deal of attention—attention that has ranged the spectrum from exaggerated praise to exaggerated criticism. Under the circumstances, it would seem fitting and interesting to look into the history of a major pharmaceutical firm and see how it developed, how it operates, and just what the regiment of investigators in its laboratories have accomplished. As I think the pages of this book show, I found the research record of the Upjohn Company impres-

sive. Its scientific and medical staff has contributed substantially to medical advance.

This book could not, of course, have been written without
the cooperation and help of the Upjohn Company and some
hundreds of its executives and employees. I can mention only
a few by name: Dr. Lawrence N. Upjohn, honorary chairman,
whose willingness to look at the old days without rose-colored
glasses I especially enjoyed; Donald S. Gilmore, chairman and
managing director; Dr. E. Gifford Upjohn, president; Dr.
Richard S. Schreiber, the director of the company's scientific
activities. I owe special thanks, in addition, to the two men
through whom my contacts with the company were funneled
—Leslie D. Harrop, vice-president and general counsel, and
William H. Bayliss, public relations manager. Many individuals in other pharmaceutical companies, in the industry association and trade publications, and in medical schools were
also generous with their time and willingness to answer questions. Further, I acknowledge gratefully the assistance of my
secretary, Ina Stuart Meyers, who not only typed the manu-
script and prepared the index but did the "legwork"—the difficult part—of the drug origins survey in Chapter 2. And once
more, I pay tribute to my wife, Kay, for her cheerful endurance
of many hours of my thinking out loud.

Finally, it goes without saying that none of the people I
spoke with has any responsibility for opinions in this book. I
wrote the book, not they.

Leonard Engel

Contents

Preface   v

1. What Has Medicine Accomplished?   1
2. The Steeds of Progress   7
3. The Inventive Doctor   22
4. Dr. W. E.'s "Big Thing"   40
5. Beginning of Upjohn Research   49
6. Vitamin Venture   67
7. A Problem of Succession   80
8. Wartime Work   92
9. The Long Hormone Road   104
10. To Cortisone and Beyond   128
11. Architecture and Antibiotics   156
12. Breakthrough on Diabetes   171
13. The Many Sides of Modern Pharmaceutical Research   191
14. The Critical Test   204

15. Pharmaceutical Engineering   215
16. Even Medicines Must Be Sold   225
17. Medicine Makers of Kalamazoo   235
18. The Useful Cycle   249
Index   255

1 | What Has Medicine Accomplished?

About a dozen years ago, a New York newspaper columnist named Albert Deutsch, irritated at the use of such slogans as "1 out of 8 will die" from this or that disease by agencies appealing for money for medical research, wrote: "The truth is that 1 out of 1 will die, no matter what we do."

Deutsch's tart comment is a useful reminder of a simple fact that tends to slip out of sight in a time of highly publicized medical advance. Medicine seeks to cure or prevent disease, promote health, and postpone death. For the moment at least, when the phrase "prevent death" is used, what is meant is the prevention of premature death. No physician or medical scientist entertains the idea that death may be prevented indefinitely or, under present circumstances, even

1

postponed for most persons much beyond seventy-five or eighty years of age. What medicine hopes to accomplish is to assure a healthful span of that number of years to all.

Within this limitation, the last several generations have seen medical progress without precedent. Seventy-five years ago, the science of bacteriology was in its infancy. Koch had just discovered the tubercle bacillus; the microbes responsible for typhoid fever, cholera, diphtheria, anthrax, and several other deadly infectious diseases were also known. But the pneumococcus (principal cause of pneumonia), *Pasteurella pestis* (responsible for bubonic plague), and the syphilis spirochete had yet to be identified. Knowledge of viruses lay even farther in the future, and a year or two was still to pass before Pasteur would save the life of Joseph Meister, the Alsatian boy, with rabies vaccine, the first new vaccine since Jenner's discovery of smallpox vaccine in 1798. In the operating room, there were still surgeons who saw no need for precautions to prevent wounds from becoming infected during surgery; and such a commonplace operation of the present day as appendectomy had never been performed. (Indeed, appendicitis was not recognized as a distinct, and lethal, disease until 1886.) In the diagnosis of disease, the doctor was largely confined to what he could learn by questioning the patient, by examining the patient's body from the outside, and by listening to the chest and heart sounds with the stethoscope (invented by Laënnec of France in 1831); diagnostic X-ray and laboratory tests belonged to the future.

The limited medical knowledge was reflected in the public health. During the previous century and a half, health had slowly improved in America and Western Europe as a result of improvements in food supply, the introduction of central water supply and sewage disposal systems, and higher standards of personal hygiene. (The custom of bathing, all but dead for centuries, had come back.) But life was still much shorter than it is today. The average expectation of life at birth in the United States of the 1880s, according to the best estimates, was somewhere between forty and forty-five years. Cemeteries of that time tell the story. Only a few graves are those of men and women who lived to a ripe old age. Most are of persons who died in their forties, their twenties, in childhood.

In the cities, tens of thousands bore the feverish glow that foretold death from tuberculosis—"the disease which medicine never cured, wealth never warded off," Charles Dickens had said in *Nicholas Nickleby*. The tuberculosis death rate was at least twenty times what it is today. Cholera still occurred, and typhoid fever was common. Ships from the West Indies brought the yellow fever mosquito and yellow fever to United States Atlantic ports almost every summer. Diphtheria, meningitis, food-borne infections, and a seemingly inexhaustible variety of severe respiratory ailments took a heavy toll of infants and children.

However drawn, the health picture is almost unrecognizably different and better in many parts of the world today. In the United States and other industrialized countries, life expectancy at birth is approaching seventy years. For women in several of these countries—women generally outlive men, for reasons that are far from clear—life expectancy is already seventy-two years or more.

The gains have been brought about by broad advances along many fronts. Nearly all of us are familiar with the rollback of infectious disease. With some conspicuous exceptions,

such as the common cold, effective means of control now
exist—and have been put to wide use—for the control of almost all infectious diseases of significance to public health,
whether caused by bacteria, viruses, or other types of para-
sites. Notable advances have been made in the care of mothers
during childbirth. Maternal death rates in the United States
have declined from 6.1 for every 1,000 live births in 1915
(when computation of maternal mortality rates in the United
States began) to fewer than 1 per 2,000 births; well-run hospitals frequently record 5,000 or more deliveries in succession
without the death of a mother. In favored parts of the world,
nutritional deficiency diseases have all but disappeared. Aided
by better diets and vitamin supplements, children burst with
vigor and good health. Ailments ranging from asthma to high
blood pressure, diabetes to rheumatoid arthritis are relieved
by hormones and other potent drugs, either obtained from
natural sources or manufactured by chemical synthesis. Lifesaving surgery has penetrated the last anatomical frontiers;
surgeons even operate within the heart.

There are many ways of measuring progress in health. Let
us use just two. One is a favorite method of professional
workers in public health—the comparison of death rates
then and now for groups of different ages in the population.
In 1900, an average of 162.4 of every 1,000 infants—nearly 1
in every 6—born in the United States died before their first
birthday. In 1958, the latest year for which figures are available, the death rate for infants under one year of age in the
United States was 29.8 per 1,000, a decline of more than 80
per cent. Among children between one and four years of age,
the death rate has fallen from 19.8 per 1,000 in 1900 to 1.1 in
1958; in the five-to-fourteen-year age group, from 3.6 to 0.5
per 1,000; in the fifteen-to-twenty-four-year age group, from

5.6 to 1.1. Other age groups have experienced similar, though considerably smaller, decreases in mortality.

Our other index of progress is a very short story. In 1918, a new type of influenza virus appeared. Since it was new, man possessed no defensive antibodies against it, and it spread with great rapidity through the world. In little more than a year, it killed half a million persons in the United States and 20 million in the rest of the world, chiefly through pneumonia, which physicians were nearly powerless to treat.

Thirty-nine years later, another new strain of influenza virus, Asian virus, made an appearance and spread with equal rapidity through the world. One in every four persons in the United States was affected. But the loss of life was quite small—hardly to be compared with the 1918–1919 pandemic at all. Specialists feel that the Asian influenza virus may have been less virulent than the 1918 virus. But the much smaller loss of life was due also to progress in the intervening years. A high-speed immunization campaign, made possible by new vaccine production techniques, gave partial protection to especially susceptible persons. Antibiotics curbed secondary infections, such as pneumonia, brought on by the influenza.

Great as they are, however, these and other achievements of medicine and public health should not be allowed to obscure the fact that numerous and formidable health problems remain. To begin with, the benefits of modern medicine and public health have yet to reach more than half the human race. There are, even in advanced countries, groups whose health is below attainable standards. American death and illness rates would be appreciably lower, for instance, if the figures for nonwhites matched those for whites and if the states with the poorest health and medical services raised themselves to the level of the best.

No less challenging is the emergence of new health problems as old ones are solved. As Dr. René Dubos, the distinguished Rockefeller Institute researcher and medical philosopher, has pointed out, disease is a result of the interaction of man and his environment. Each age in history accordingly has its characteristic diseases—ours no less than the ages that have gone before.

In our time, two great problems are cancer and degenerative diseases of the heart and blood vessels. In country after country, they have emerged as the leading causes of death. In part, this has come about through the decrease in other causes of death; many more people are now living long enough to develop cancer, heart disease, and other ailments of middle or later life. But cancer and heart disease are also responsible for many premature deaths. Moreover, the occurrence of many cases late in life diminishes neither the urgency nor the complexity of cancer and heart disease as health problems.

In addition, there is the great problem of emotional and mental illness and the host of "minor" (but costly) illnesses, such as the common cold. Finally, progress in medicine inevitably raises numerous new problems, such as previously undetected diseases (the "new" diseases caused by recently discovered viruses are an example) and the maintenance of health and vigor in a population with an ever-larger proportion of persons in the late years of life.

But the existence of unsolved health problems is also only one side of the coin. One ought not lose sight of the other—the fundamental transformation in human health effected by the health sciences in the short span of seventy-five years.

2 | The Steeds of Progress

The remarkable changes in health during the past several generations have been the work of many individuals, some of whom are not usually thought of as contributors to health and who certainly had not the least idea that their labors would help roll back disease. Thus, the Duryeas and Henry Fords were merely interested in perfecting an alternate to the railroad train and the horse. Their invention, the automobile, has proved a fearful killer and maimer but, on balance, has saved many more lives than it has blighted, by forcing the paving of streets and roads. In the 1880s, the United States was covered each summer by a layer of dust rich in horse manure, a prime breeding ground for germs. The paving simultaneously eliminated the dust and the breeding ground for a vast swarm of noxious agents responsible for many severe infections which struck particularly at children. (Even if automobile exhaust is finally implicated in lung cancer, we shall still be ahead. Lung cancer still does not cause nearly as many deaths as were due, in the old days, to dust-borne infections.) Improvement to health figured large as a motive in the development of the refrigerator and other innovations that have added to and improved food supply. But housing—an important factor in health—has been improved because bad, overcrowded housing is a social pest. And devices like the electric dishwasher were introduced largely as conveniences; the dishwasher, though, is also a health aid, because it washes dishes with water at pasteurizing temperatures and dries them without the assistance of that marvelous means of spreading germs from one member of a family to another, the dish towel.

But the gain in health is chiefly due to the increase of knowledge in medicine and public health and allied fields. The virtual disappearance of diseases like typhoid fever is a direct result of the discovery that germ-laden water may be made safe to drink by treating it with chlorine. Similarly, the immunizing vaccines that provide further protection against many ills have been the fruit of research on bacteria and viruses. More recently, profound new knowledge from many branches of science has given the physician unprecedented power to deal with disease.

Medicine and public health have advanced with almost overwhelming speed on four stout steeds. One is the study of the structure and functioning of the body in health and disease. Another is the search for specific agents that cause disease. The third is the development of methods of diagnosing and exactly identifying a patient's illness, for a patient can be treated effectively only if his illness is known. The fourth is the discovery of drugs and other means of treating disease.

The four lines of medical advance have moved forward together, but not always at the same speed. They have also involved different kinds of scientific investigators and institutions. Research on methods of diagnosis has been carried on mainly by physicians in medical schools and large hospitals, because new methods of diagnosis can be worked out only where there are patients. Physicians have likewise made many distinguished contributions to knowledge of the working of the body. But the lead passed some decades ago to researchers in other disciplines: physiology, nutrition, embryology, genetics, histology (the microscopic study of tissues). Lately, the most significant contributions have come from biochemists adept at unraveling the body's chemical machinery. Moreover, the institutions where these basic biological and physiological researchers work have broadened as well. At one time, most research was confined to a small number of medical schools and other institutes. Now the army of scientists probing the machinery of the body may be found at work in many more schools and institutes, and in a great number of government and pharmaceutical laboratories as well. The third avenue to medical advance— research on basic causes of disease—is being pursued by an even larger number of workers from the various biological sciences and is under way in an even more varied list of research centers.

The discovery of new drugs and other means of treating disease, such as surgery, is another matter. In the field of surgery, the surgeon alone can introduce new procedures. So most advances in surgery have come from medical schools and hospitals. To make progress, though, the surgeon has also had to go back to the laboratory. Nearly all significant developments in surgery today stem from research in the animal laboratory.

As to new drugs and medicinal agents, progress was comparatively slow until a little more than a generation ago. Morphine, quinine, and digitalis had long been known. Aspirin's pain-relieving properties were discovered in 1898. Epinephrine, thyroid hormone, and insulin were isolated between 1898 and 1921. The same general period saw the development of important vaccines.

In 1900, German bacteriologists discovered pyocyanase, a substance we would call an "antibiotic." Pyocyanase was generated by a microbe and was used to treat patients with diphtheria, anthrax, and other infectious diseases. Its success in many cases caused a sensation. But the science and technology of 1900–1910 were not up to putting out pyocyanase in pure, consistently effective form, and the antibiotic spark went out, not to be rekindled until World War II. It was nearly the same with Paul Ehrlich's famous forecast of man-made chemical bullets against disease microbes. No other chemical bullets against disease followed the antisyphilis drugs, salvarsan and neosalvarsan, devised by Ehrlich.

The era of rapid advance in drugs began in 1934 with the discovery of sulfanilamide, the first sulfa compound. In the United States, the blue book of drugs is the United States Pharmacopoeia; only medicinal agents reflecting the best in medical teaching and practice are included. In the thirty years before sulfanilamide, the number of new drugs admitted to the Pharmacopoeia averaged only six per year. Since sulfanilamide, the yearly average has been thirty-seven.

Since physicians alone can assume the responsibility of testing drugs in patients and working out methods of use, doctors have been intimately involved in the development of new drugs. As in many other areas of medical research, however, much of the basic work leading to new drugs was and is done by men and women outside medicine. Hormones and other natural substances that have become medicines came from basic research upon the machinery of the body. Antibiotics are found by microbiologists. Chemists produce ever larger numbers of potent new medicinal agents by modifying natural substances or creating entirely new ones.

Pharmaceutical companies and their people have long been involved in the development of new drugs, if in no other way, then in solving the many problems attending the manufacture of drugs. Further, during the past generation, researchers in pharmaceutical laboratories have become the chief discoverers of drugs. At least three-quarters of the drugs and medicinal agents now in use were initially discovered in pharmaceutical industry laboratories or, in a small percentage of cases, by outside researchers working with pharmaceutical industry financial support.

In the course of preparing this book, the origins of 210 drugs and other medicinal agents in current use were looked into. The survey, which is summarized in the table below, covered antibiotics and other antibacterials, hormones and hormone derivatives, vitamins, antihistamines, tranquilizers, sedatives, pain relievers, antihypertensives, diuretics, anticoagulants, and several other classes of drugs—in short, a sizable majority of the different drugs (not different preparations of the same drugs) doctors were prescribing at the time the survey was made. Three criteria were followed in selecting drugs for inclusion in the tally. The drug had to have a substantial volume of sale or show other evidence of importance in medicine. (For example, several products with a

ORIGINS OF DRUGS IN CURRENT USE

Type of product	Industry origin		Industry participation		Other		Total	
	No.	%	No.	%	No.	%	No.	%
Anti-infectives	41	..	1	.	8	..	50	...
Hormone products ...	16	..	3	.	16	..	35	...
Nutritionals	5	..	2	.	6	..	13	...
Other pharmacologic products	87	..	3	.	22	..	112	...
Total	149	71	9	4	52	25	210	100

relatively small sale, but with highly specialized, indispensable uses, were included.) There had to be documentary evidence of the drug's origin, such as patents or reports in journals of original publication. The affiliation of the discoverer also had to be clear. (Only a small number of drugs actually had to be excluded because evidence of origin or of the discoverer's affiliations could not be located.)

One hundred forty-nine, or 71 per cent, of the 210 were discovered in pharmaceutical laboratories. Nine (4 per cent) were found by outside investigators working under grants or on some other financial arrangement with the pharmaceutical industry. Fifty-two (25 per cent) were found by investigators working in medical schools, research institutes, or other laboratories without commercial support.

The roster of drugs discovered by pharmaceutical industry investigators reads like a "who's who" of familiar names. Most of the antibiotic "mycins." All of the hydrocortisone derivatives in current use for treating arthritis and related disorders. Orinase, the first oral drug for the treatment of diabetes to become available and still the most effective. Chlorpromazine, the compound that opened up the drug treatment of mental illness. The most universally used of all medicinal agents, aspirin.

The preponderance of pharmaceutical laboratories in some areas of drug research is almost startling, especially in recently opened-up fields like antibiotics. Of nineteen antibiotics in current use, thirteen (including all the broad-spectrum antibiotics) were found by investigators in pharmaceutical laboratories or by outside scientists working with industry support. Of the sulfonamides, all (including sulfanilamide itself) were discovered in industrial laboratories. In areas in which synthetic chemicals predominate (such as tranquilizers, antihistamines, and the like), 90 per cent are of industrial origin.

The pharmaceutical industry contribution as originator has been least—but still highly significant—in fields that were opened up before the growth of pharmaceutical research. Thus, the majority of basic hormone discoveries were made outside the industry; but the proportion of significant pharmaceutical industry discoveries has increased as pharmaceutical industry chemists have become more interested in, and more clever at, creating hormone derivatives that outdo nature. Similarly, many vitamin discoveries were made at a time when pharmaceutical industry research was in its infancy. But the two most significant recent advances in nutrition—the discovery and isolation of folic acid and vitamin B₁₂—were both made in pharmaceutical laboratories.

In the process of becoming the major discoverer of new drugs and medicines, the pharmaceutical industry not only made a far-reaching contribution to health but completely transformed itself. The change can be gauged in many ways. The simplest is the one common yardstick for diverse goods and services, money value. In the mid-1930s, the sale of drugs in the United States totaled, at the manufacturers' level, some $250 million a year. "Proprietaries" (drugs advertised to the general public) accounted for more than half the total, as against "ethicals" (drugs not advertised to the public, in practice chiefly prescription drugs). In 1959, proprietary sales were about $450 million, and ethical drug volume, close to $2 billion. Allowing for drugstore markups, United States consumers were spending well over $3 billion a year for drugs and medicines.

The pharmaceutical industry's tenfold growth in twenty-five years was due in part to the increase in United States population, especially the increase in the number of Americans at the two extremes of life. (The very young and very old consume a more than proportionate share of many drug products.) But the major factor was the flood of new discoveries. In 1959, sales of antibiotics for human use totaled (at the manufacturers' level) nearly $400 million. Antibiotics did not exist in the 1930s, nor did cortisone and its derivatives (annual sale now approaching $100 million), antihistamines (1959 sale, $40 million), or tranquilizers (1959 volume, over $200 million). Vitamins and related nutritional products, barely arrived on the scene in 1930, are now manufactured at a rate of $250 million worth a year. Sulfas, first introduced in the United States in 1937, still have a sale of over $40 million annually, despite the emergence of the antibiotics.

Notwithstanding its extraordinary growth, however, the pharmaceutical industry is far from large as American industries go. As recently as 1958, there were 16 corporations on the *Fortune* list of the 500 largest United States corporations whose individual sales were larger than the sales of the entire ethical segment of the pharmaceutical industry taken together. According to the 1954 Census of Manufactures— the most recent authoritative count available—the pharmaceutical industry had fewer than 100,000 employees. (But among them were 3,000 with graduate degrees in sciences.)

The pharmaceutical pie, moreover, is cut into many pieces. Drugs and medicines are manufactured by more than 1,100 companies. In marked contrast to the automobile, steel, and numerous other industries, the largest pharmaceutical firm accounts for less than 12 per cent of the industry's total business. The six largest pharmaceutical firms today have a smaller share of over-all sales than the six largest a half-century ago.

The pharmaceutical industry is not easy to describe because drug firms originated in many different ways and can have bewilderingly varied form. Some—Merck & Co., Inc., is a well-known example—began as manufacturers of fine chemicals, then branched into, or merged with, companies already established in the finished pharmaceutical field. One large firm, Chas. Pfizer & Co., capitalized on experience in producing chemicals by fermentation processes to enter the manufacture of antibiotics and, from that vantage point, the production of other pharmaceuticals. Many manufacturers began as compounders of finished pharmaceuticals from medicinal chemicals purchased from other firms and only later entered basic medicinal chemical production themselves; the most prominent of these firms is the Upjohn Company of Kalamazoo, Michigan, founded in 1885 by a country doctor, Dr. W. E. Upjohn. Vaccines furnished the starting point for several other drug houses and patent medicines for still others. The largest number of pharmaceutical companies began with the development of a specialty product or two, perhaps by a pharmacist, chemist, or physician.

Pharmaceutical companies may be "long-line" houses producing hundreds of different products, or specialty houses turning out a few dozen. (Hardly any pharmaceutical firm manufactures only one or two products any more. Present-day costs are too high to permit such firms to survive. They either develop or acquire additional products or disappear.) Many large pharmaceutical firms manufacture medicinal chemicals both for their own use and for sale to other drug houses. Many also produce nonpharmaceutical products: basic chemicals, laboratory reagents, livestock feed supplements, agricultural chemicals, veterinary products. Pharmaceutical firms may be independent enterprises or divisions of larger corporations. Thus, two of the best-known United States houses, E. R. Squibb & Son and Lederle Laboratories, are divisions of large chemical combines (Olin-Mathieson and American Cyanamid, respectively). Other drug houses are held by firms with interests in the cosmetics and miscellaneous home products fields. Conversely, some medicinals are turned out by firms with just a toe in the drug field; a chemical company with essentially no other pharmaceutical interests is one of the largest United States bulk producers of aspirin.

The patterns of business and ownership in the pharmaceutical industry can be confusing enough to cause statisticians to reach for the headache and ulcer remedies that constitute two of the industry's most widely sold products. There are even firms that produce nothing but intermediate compounds that other firms will finish into basic medicinal chemicals (which they may either sell to someone else or finish into pharmaceuticals themselves), and "private-formula" houses that manufacture and package products under someone else's label (usually a drugstore chain, a department store, or a mail-order house). Probably the most meaningful distinction is between the proprietary and ethical branches of the industry. The distinction is based on advertising policy and goes back to the patent medicine era. In order to set themselves clearly apart from the patent medicine men—and, among other things, add to their own standing with the medical profession—ethical houses adopted a policy of not advertising to the general public. Firms that manufacture prescription drugs continue to promote their wares only to physicians, though many also sell over-the-counter products which could be advertised to the public. In fact, ethical firms may soon be advertising vitamin products, because of recent losses in sales to companies, in and out of the pharmaceutical industry, that shout vitamins from the housetops.

Federal law and a more sophisticated era have made proprietary companies essentially manufacturers of simple home remedies. But the distinction between proprietary and ethical drugs still has force—perhaps even greater force than years ago. The outstanding characteristic of the important drugs developed in recent years is their potency. The latter makes most of them unsuitable for over-the-counter sale and they are, in fact, generally sold on a doctor's prescription only and advertised to physicians alone. In any event, where pharmaceutical firms produce both proprietary and prescription drugs, the two types of product are usually handled by different divisions. The big growth in the pharmaceutical industry has come in prescription drugs.

What are some other characteristics of the pharmaceutical industry? It is an industry like other industries in that it operates to make a profit. A few firms have made exceptional profits. But the great majority, even of the larger firms, have had profits comparable to those of corporations in many other industries. A recent study showed that seven leading pharmaceutical firms (including three that had unusually large earnings during the period in question and one whose earnings had been poorer than usual) had had gross profits per dollar of sales between 1952 and 1956 almost exactly equal to the profit per dollar of sale of the largest corporations in the automobile, chemical, petroleum, and steel industries.

The achievement of that record is of interest because pharmaceutical research and development involve greater than ordinary financial risks. During the 1950s, new prescription products were marketed at a rate of about four hundred a year, including different forms and combinations of previously known as well as new drugs. All but a few have had a market life of but two to five years, during which their development and marketing costs had to be regained, before displacement by improved products. "The pharmaceutical industry," remarked the president of a leading drug house, "lives in the shadow of its own obsolescence."

Of course, many of the new drugs marketed each year do not represent significant additions to the physician's arsenal. It is quite impossible, however, to draw up a set of rules which will infallibly prevent the introduction of new drugs of little value, yet not block useful new drugs. Moreover, it is not just trivial drugs that disappear quickly. Obsolescence often strikes most swiftly at important new drugs; their very importance spurs intense efforts to find still more effective agents. This has been the case, for example, with sulfonamides, antibiotics, drugs for high blood pressure, and many hormones.

The possibility of substantial financial loss as a result is no figment of the imagination. Since World War II, almost every major pharmaceutical house has had the experience of losing virtually overnight all or most of the market for a leading product. This has happened, among others, to the manufacturers of the first three broad-spectrum antibiotics, two of the first companies to produce cortisone and its derivatives, a producer of vaccines, and several of the early manufacturers of antihistamines. Further, while research and new-drug costs have been rising (in keeping with the general rise in medical costs as a result of the development of more elaborate tools and methods of medical care), intense competition has brought down and held down the prices of older drugs. The penicillin and streptomycin price drop (which forced all but the largest, most efficient producers out of the field) is well known. In addition, products like the broad-spectrum antibiotics have come down 65 per cent in price since 1949; and cortisone and related hormone products have continued to decline to a present (1960) level of but 5 to 7 per cent of cortisone's introductory price in 1950. And the prices of such standard items as aspirin have remained almost unchanged for more than two decades.

Strenuous competition has caused a sizable increase in pharmaceutical company efforts to persuade physicians to prescribe their products. The most significant result of the competition, however, has been the progressive expansion of pharmaceutical research. The most effective insurance a pharmaceutical company can have against the risks of a rapidly moving industry is a program for being first on the market—second may get only the leavings—with the successors to its own products or at least with equally marketable alternates. The pharmaceutical industry accordingly has recently reinvested 8 to 10 per cent of its dollar sales in research, as compared with 3 per cent for American industry as a whole. In dollars, current pharmaceutical research expenditures total nearly $200 million a year. With that sum, the industry, in addition to carrying on numerous other research undertakings, investigates well over 100,000 different chemical substances (many thousands of them synthesized in pharmaceutical laboratories) a year to find the small number (40 or so in an average year's work) that will make useful new drugs and the one new drug every few years that represents a breakthrough.

The growth of pharmaceutical research has made the industry a significant new vehicle for medical research. Let us see how this developed and how the modern pharmaceutical industry took shape by going back into the record of one pharmaceutical company—the Upjohn Company of Kalamazoo, Michigan. In the seventy-five years since its founding, Upjohn has become not only a major United States manufacturer of pharmaceuticals with annual sales of over $150 million and a line of over five hundred different products, but a major center for research on hormones, antidiabetics, antibiotics, and in other key fields.

3 | The Inventive Doctor

In 1885, when the Upjohn Pill and Granule Company —as the Upjohn Company was known at first—opened for business, such exciting discoveries as the identification of the tuberculosis germ and the germs responsible for a number of other diseases were beginning to lay the basis for scientific medicine. But not too much had as yet been learned that could be directly applied to curing the sick, and much of the practice of medicine was as it had been for decades. Likewise, the modern pharmaceutical industry was hardly to be discerned in the ragtag of means by which medicines were produced and dispensed to the public. Several pharmaceutical houses prominent today were already in existence, but none were the multimillion-dollar firms they are now. The largest

22

drug manufacturers were wholesale druggists engaged in manufacturing drugs on the side. A substantial share of the medicines dispensed by the physician were compounded by the doctor himself, especially in rural areas. Drugstores also prepared many of the remedies they sold.

Many of the medicines on the markets were the secret-formula medicines misnamed "patent" medicines, as a hangover of the days when kings granted monopolies, or "patents," for the manufacture of secret medicinal concoctions. (The modern patent is also an exclusive license to manufacture, but it is issued only in return for disclosure of the invention patented. Drugs are frequently patented; however, the formula must be disclosed. So far as known, only one secret-formula "patent medicine" concoction actually received a United States patent.) In the 1880s, no law limited the claims for patent medicines or required the naming of ingredients or restricted what might be put into them. The result was what Stewart H. Holbrook, expert chronicler of the odd side of American history, has termed the Golden Age of Quackery. Bitter herbs were dressed up as Donald McKay's Indian Worm Eradicator, Autumn Leaf Extract for Females, and several hundred other preparations with equally flamboyant titles. Syrups containing morphine were sold as tuberculosis cures; alcohol was used so liberally in numerous nostrums that more alcohol was sold (according to one disgusted physician) as medicine than as a beverage.

If less hazardous than the patent medicines, most of the drugs dispensed by the physician were not much more effective. Moreover, although specifications for basic medicines were spelled out, then as now, in the United States Pharmacopoeia, drugs with uniform, predictable properties were often hard to obtain. The difficulties ranged from unexpected variations in strength to liquids of appalling unpalatability and pills so hard they passed through the patient without dissolving.

The Upjohn Pill and Granule Company came into being as the result of an invention designed to solve one of these problems: the pills that were too hard. The invention was an ingenious new method of making pills; the inventor, Dr. William Erastus Upjohn, a thirty-one-year-old physician practicing in Hastings, Michigan, a farming community and county seat 125 miles west of Detroit.

Dr. Upjohn, who was born June 5, 1853, was the son of a physician, Dr. Uriah Upjohn, who settled and practiced in Richland, a village near Kalamazoo, a town which soon became one of the larger centers in western Michigan. A native of England, Dr. Uriah had visited the United States in 1830, when he was twenty-two, to see whether his family ought to emigrate to the United States or Australia. Two years later, he came to the United States for good, obtained a medical degree at the College of Physicians and Surgeons in New York, and moved West.

Dr. Uriah began practice in Richland in 1835. He and his wife—daughter of a pioneer settler in the area—had twelve children, eleven of whom survived. When the brood reached high school and college age, Dr. Uriah rented a house at the edge of the University of Michigan campus in Ann Arbor and put an older daughter in charge. Then, as each youngster reached the appropriate age, he or she was dispatched to the house in Ann Arbor to attend either high school or the university or both. The oldest daughter, Helen, and three of the four boys—Henry U., the oldest son; William E., the

William Erastus Upjohn, M.D. Elected president 1887; was chairman of the board and managing director from 1930 until his death in 1932.

Lawrence N. Upjohn, M.D. Elected president 1930; chairman of the board 1943; honorary chairman 1952.

The pharmaceutical production building in the foreground, completed in 1951, and fine chemical and fermentation plants in the background, are located on 1,700 acre site south of Kalamazoo.

Office building in downtown Kalamazoo and research tower rising thirteen floors directly behind it were constructed in 1936.

second son; and James T., the youngest—all became doctors. Dr. Henry's wife, Dr. Millie Kirby Upjohn, was a doctor to boot.

The Upjohn children spent their childhood on a farm, where the boys all had early and frequent occasion to repair and improvise farm equipment. The contact with farm implements brought out in them a strong mechanical and inventive bent. Dr. Henry, whose medical practice was in Kalamazoo, had a workshop in his home and worked on inventions in his spare time. He devised a knot-tyer for hay-binding machines (sold to a major producer of farm equipment for $1,500), a feed cutter, a cultivator resembling the modern disc cultivator, and a shock-absorbing mounting for buggy shafts.

Soon after settling in Hastings, Dr. William E. (or Dr. W. E., as he was more often called), Dr. Henry's younger brother, became interested in an arrangement for making a series of electric "slave" clocks keep uniform time by means of a master clock. Another and more fruitful interest was Dr. W. E.'s novel process for making pills. Instead of forming them from a paste—the usual way—Dr. W. E. built them up from "starter" particles in a revolving pan, by alternately spraying the starter particles with moistening agents and sifting powdered drugs onto them. The procedure produced a pill whose medicinal ingredients could be precisely controlled and that needed no gums or adhesives to hold together. Further, Dr. W. E.'s pill, unlike others in use at the time, could be crumbled with the thumb and could be relied on to break up and deliver its charge of medicine within the patient's body.

Dr. W. E. applied for a patent on his process for making

"friable" pills—as he termed them—in 1884. The patent,
No. 312,041, was granted January 10, 1885. But he actually
began making pills by his process in the attic of his home in
1883.

The pill business—which Dr. W. E. carried on mornings,
while he continued with medical practice in the afternoon
and evening—soon outgrew the attic. So the inventive physician moved his "factory" to the upper floor of an abandoned
Hastings feed mill, where he had not only more space but
power to turn his pans.

The friable pills continued to meet with a ready sale. As a
result, in less than a year, Dr. W. E. had to look again for new
quarters and also for capital for expansion. This time, he
consulted Dr. Henry, his brother in Kalamazoo. The outcome was the formation of a partnership, to be known as the
Upjohn Pill and Granule Company, and the moving of the
business to Kalamazoo. Later, the two younger brothers,
Frederick L. (the one who did not become a doctor though
he later studied pharmacy) and Dr. James Upjohn, were
added as partners.

The new firm began operations late in 1885 in the basement of the Upjohn Block, a block of stores with apartments
and offices above, which Dr. Henry had put up near Burdick
Street, one of Kalamazoo's main streets, a few years before.
The next year, the new company had a building of its own, a
2½-story square brick structure measuring 36 feet on a side,
on a site behind the Upjohn Block now occupied by a Wool-
worth store.

For many years, the Upjohn Company has used the slogan,
"Fine Pharmaceuticals Since 1886," in its advertisements and
catalogues. The date refers to the issuance of its first printed

price list a few months after the actual formation of the company late in 1885. The price list, a single page printed in small type, presented a total of 186 pill formulas compounded from 56 different drugs: 30 botanicals, 20 chemicals, 5 alkaloids, and 1 glucoside.

The formulas for the pills were similar to many put out by other drug houses. They included quinine pills, a popular nineteenth-century remedy for all sorts of chills and fevers as well as for malaria; a Blaud iron pill for use as an iron tonic; and "Pills, Anti-Constipation, Upjohn," a laxative that was soon in quite wide use. In addition, there were a number of medications in the form of "granules"—small pills containing half a grain of medication or less.

The Upjohn products were distinguished by two features. One was quality. In the 1880s and for several decades thereafter, the drug industry was marked by exceedingly severe price competition. No firm could meet all competitors on the basis of price alone and expect to survive. Upjohn accordingly determined to establish a reputation for quality from the very beginning—a fact reflected in signs long posted throughout the Upjohn plant: "Keep the quality up—W. E. Upjohn."

The other distinguishing feature of the fledgling company's pills was their novel method of manufacture and their friability. To emphasize the ease with which they could be reduced to powder, Upjohn adopted as its trademark a drawing of Dr. W. E.'s thumb crushing a pill. The trademark not only helped establish the company name. It gave Dr. W. E. the most widely reproduced thumb in history. In one form or another, the thumb trademark was used for nearly sixty years and appeared in thousands of advertisements and on tens of millions of package labels. It was kept until the end of World War II—decades after the friable pill itself had passed into history.

When the Upjohn Pill and Granule Company moved into the building behind the Upjohn Block, it had a dozen employees on its payroll, and four partners, three of whom also worked full time for the company. Dr. W. E.—who abandoned the practice of medicine entirely when the pill and granule company was organized—bought the raw materials and "introduced" the finished products to druggists, wholesalers, and dispensing physicians (doctors who stocked their own supplies of medicine). Dr. W. E. and Frederick, the non-doctor brother, devised pill counters, bottling machines, and other equipment. Frederick and Dr. James saw to production. Dr. Henry remained in active medical practice; but he was leaned on heavily for advice, for he was the most experienced businessman in the group, and he had studied pharmacy as well as medicine. Moreover, it was Dr. Henry who financed construction of the Burdick Street plant (as the building behind the Upjohn Block became known).

The second floor of the plant was used for manufacturing. At first, there were two pill-making pans; a third was added later. Two men and a woman usually tended the pans, which were turned by belts from a small kerosene-fueled steam engine down below on the first floor. Also on the first floor were a fireproof brick vault for records and valuable drugs, a packaging room, a shipping room, and the office. A bridge connected the second floor of the plant to the second floor of the Upjohn Block.

During 1886—its first full year—the pill and granule company grossed a promising $50,000. In January, 1887, however, the family and the company suffered a sudden and unexpected blow. Dr. Henry contracted typhoid fever, of which he died. Aside from the personal loss to the brothers and the loss of his counsel to the business, his death forced a reorganization of the company—the first of several reorganizations Upjohn was to undergo over the years.

Dr. Henry had had a two-fifths interest in the firm. About a month after Dr. Henry's death his widow, Dr. Millie Kirby Upjohn, sold half his share to Dr. James Upjohn and the other half to four new partners. Two of the latter were Dr. Henry D. Jones, a distant relative from East Chatham, New York, and John M. Gilmore, Kalamazoo dry goods merchant and uncle of a subsequent president and board chairman of the Upjohn Company. Dr. James and the new partners paid a total of $8,000 for their rights.

The sale of Dr. Henry's share necessitated the drawing of a new partnership agreement, signed on the day of the sale. The most interesting feature is a clause specifying that the three surviving Upjohn brothers were to work full time for the company and listing their salaries. Dr. W. E., as head of the firm, was to receive $1,200 a year; Frederick was to receive $900; and Dr. James, $600.

Later that year, the partnership was dissolved and the firm incorporated as a joint stock company with capital stock of $60,000 and with the former partners receiving shares of stock in proportion to their share in the partnership. Dr. W. E. was elected president; Dr. James, vice-president; Frederick, secretary; and John Gilmore became treasurer.

Over the next several years, friable pills continued to find an expanding market, enabling the Upjohn Pill and Granule

Company to grow steadily. In 1888, the firm was compelled to build a larger plant—a four-story brick building on East Lovell Street, first of the large group of buildings Upjohn was gradually to erect between Lovell Street and Portage Road in downtown Kalamazoo. The new plant was called Building no. 4, for counting the Hastings feed mill as no. 1, it was the fourth location in which Upjohn products had been manufactured. (Building no. 4 was torn down after World War II to make way for a badly needed parking lot.) In 1890, Upjohn sales reached $132,500.

Actually, the period of prosperity was short lived. In 1891, competitors introduced the compressed tablet, made by simply compressing powdered drugs into tablet-shaped molds with, when needed, a binder to provide adhesion. Although three decades were to pass before the pharmaceutical industry finally learned how to put accurately measured doses into tablets, the compressed tablet quickly became popular. Five grains of medicine—a common dose—are easier to swallow as a flat tablet than in a round pill.

The Upjohn Company sought to meet the new competition in two ways. One was by entrance into the buyer's-label and special formula business. The other was broadening of the Upjohn line to include other medicinals besides pills.

"Buyer's-label" goods are standard products labeled with the buyer's name in return for an order of specified size. "Special-formula" goods are products made up in bulk to the order of a buyer who packages and distributes them himself. Many pharmaceutical firms still do buyer's-label and special-formula business.

As buyer's-label goods, Upjohn offered popular remedies of the day and variants on a number of its own products:

cathartic pills, kidney pills, cold remedies, cough syrups, digestant tablets, and the like. For special-formula customers, the Kalamazoo company made a variety of medicinal products. Of these, the most important was a small laxative pill produced for the Sydney Ross Company, an enterprise started by Frederick Upjohn and a friend. The latter, a shoe salesman who had traveled extensively in Latin America, became convinced that a cathartic pill, of a type widely used in the United States, would also sell well in Latin America. He persuaded Frederick, and the Sydney Ross Company was the result. The name of the company came from a gravestone in a cemetery they chanced to visit on a Sunday bicycle trip.

The friend's hunch was good. The small laxative pill caught on at once in Latin America. Eventually, the Sydney Ross Company—which was finally absorbed by a larger drug firm in the 1920s—came to have a plant of its own in Brazil. For two decades, however, Upjohn supplied Sydney Ross with its laxative pills, at a rate that sometimes reached 15 million pills a month.

At the same time, Upjohn began adding to the variety of products put out under its own name. Hypodermic tablets—for the preparation of hypodermic injections—appeared on the Upjohn price list for the first time in 1891. Since many of these tablets were made from powdered extracts, the latter were also offered for sale. Next, in 1892, came another widely used group of medicinals, "fluidextracts"—extracts of herbs and botanicals concentrated so that a pint of extract contained the active drug from a pound of raw material. Finally, the Upjohn line was expanded to include tinctures (fluidextracts reduced, usually, to one-tenth fluidextract strength), elixirs (spiced and sweetened fluidextracts and tinctures fortified with alcohol), cordials (elixirs by a more elegant name), syrups, medicated wines, and ointments. By 1900, more than 700 items were listed in the Upjohn catalogue.

The new products transformed Upjohn from a pill and granule maker into a general manufacturer of pharmaceuticals. The change was formally signaled in 1902, when the company underwent another reorganization. Although the primary purpose of the reorganization was to raise additional capital, the occasion was used to drop pill and granule out of the company title and to give the Kalamazoo firm its present simple name: The Upjohn Company.

The buyer's-label and special-formula business and the new Upjohn products substantially increased the company's total sales without greatly helping its earnings. One difficulty was the need for enlarged manufacturing facilities. Another was the competitiveness of the buyer's-label and special-formula business. Volume was large—at one point, Upjohn was producing a million pills a day, one-third for sale under its own name and two-thirds for buyer's-label and special-formula customers. But prices were low, as low as 17 cents per 1,000 for cathartic pills, for example. In fact, Upjohn quit seeking new buyer's-label and special-formula customers shortly before World War I and, in the mid-twenties, abandoned the field altogether.

The expanded Upjohn line was itself not much more profitable. Unhappily, many of the Kalamazoo firm's new products were essentially similar to products already on the market and could not gain the kind of advantage once held by the friable pill. The situation was further complicated by the fact that many drugstores were hostile to the Upjohn Company because Upjohn also sold to dispensing physicians, whom the drugstores looked upon as competitors. Consequently, Upjohn sales were concentrated increasingly among rural dispensing physicians, who bought cheap and in small lots only.

The real solution for Upjohn's problem was the development of specialties—products sufficiently distinctive to stand out and sufficiently in demand to command a substantial sale and remunerative price. Today, pharmaceutical houses in need of specialties look to the laboratory for them. At the turn of the century, new pharmaceutical products were apt to have a more informal origin. Thus, Upjohn's first specialties since the friable pill were originated by an imaginative salesman, Frederick L. Childs, who had worked as a drug clerk and pharmacist before coming to Upjohn.

Childs had a flair for concocting catchily titled, attractive variants of standard prescription formulas. In rapid succession, shortly after 1900, he came up with Palmo-Dionin, an impressively colored sedative cough syrup; Pill Methylene Blue Compound, "The Urinary Antiseptic"; Pill Cactus Compound, "The Heart Tonic"; and Caripeptic Liquid, "The Vegetable Digestant."

Childs's creations were essentially rule-of-thumb mixtures of popular drugs whose value in medicine was scientifically unproved. But the same was true of nearly all other medicines then in use, whether prepared by a manufacturer or compounded in the drugstore's back room and whether prescribed by a physician or sold over the drugstore counter. Even physicians who suspected how little value most drugs then had prescribed them; their patients would not have had it otherwise.

Accordingly, several of Childs's preparations attained considerable sale, and one, Caripeptic Liquid, became one of the longest-lived items in the Upjohn catalogue. Caripeptic Liquid was a tastily spiced mixture of malt enzymes (to aid in the digestion of starch) and papain (an enzyme from the tropical papaya fruit, included as an aid to the digestion of protein), plus alcohol as a preservative. Nearly twenty years later, Dr. Frederick W. Heyl, Upjohn's first research director, showed that Caripeptic Liquid contained too little papain to have a significant effect on protein digestion; the claims made for Caripeptic Liquid were therefore modified. Caripeptic Liquid nevertheless went on selling at a rate of tens of thousands of dollars' worth a year. Doctors had found it not only effective in relieving mild stomach distress (despite a low papain content) but a handy vehicle for unpleasant-tasting drugs.

But the preparations devised by Childs did not do well enough wholly to offset the decline of the friable pill. As a result, the future of the Kalamazoo company remained uncertain.

One individual, however, was still at least outwardly unconcerned—the man who had invented the friable pill and who for nearly fifty years—until his death in 1932—was the Upjohn Company's moving spirit. When associates spoke of the "good old days" of the friable pill, Dr. W. E. invariably replied, "Well, the friable pill was a big thing. But never mind. One day we will have another one." A few short years were to prove him right.

The man who invented the friable pill and founded the Upjohn Company was a short stocky individual with a square face and jaw who would have found one aspect of the world of the 1960s quite strange. He was not a "corporation man." He was as firm a believer in group effort as any modern business executive. But he managed the company without back-slapping; he asked questions and conferred with associates but made decisions without calling committee meetings, and his world was not bounded by the company. He belonged to a generation in which the boss was expected to be something of an autocrat and a person who kept his own counsel, and he was both. He also had many interests outside the firm, and he retained the outlook of a physician.

During World War I, the Upjohn Company issued a magazine for its salesmen, *The Overflow* (published since September, 1923, on a regular monthly basis). Several of the early issues contained caricatures of Upjohn personalities drawn by W. Harold Upjohn, Dr. W. E.'s son. One showed Dr. W. E. himself in characteristic pose: standing with feet apart and body tilted slightly forward, a disapproving finger pointing silently toward something that had aroused his displeasure. "Dr. W. E. never bawled anyone out," Dr. Lawrence N. Upjohn, his nephew and successor as Upjohn president, recollects. "When he saw something he disliked, he spoke about it just once, or pointed at it and said nothing at all. He didn't have to say anything. You knew what he wanted."

Dr. W. E.'s reserve was owing in part to shyness. He talked well when he got started, but he found it difficult to get started in large gatherings. He even found it difficult to speak freely in the small circle of friends who gathered Sunday evenings in the Upjohn home in a residential section of Kalamazoo a half-dozen blocks from the plant. He preferred to talk to people one at a time.

Among his favorite "listening posts" were his daughters. Dr. Upjohn had a son and three daughters, all by his first wife, Rachel Babcock Upjohn, who died in 1905. In the period between Rachel Upjohn's death and Dr. W. E.'s second marriage (in 1913, to Carrie Gilmore, widow of James F. Gilmore, partner in the Gilmore Brothers department store and brother of the first treasurer of the Upjohn Company), his children served as audience for his ideas. Other favorite hearers were a few friends and two or three Upjohn Company associates.

His ideas ranged widely. He was a believing Christian but was strongly opposed to sectarianism. On one occasion, he argued so convincingly and persuasively against it that a young minister of the Upjohns' acquaintance decided—to Dr. W. E.'s utter astonishment—he could no longer teach sectarian gospel and quit the cloth.

Dr. W. E. was likewise interested in bank reform. In 1905, he worked out a plan for insuring bank deposits, which he described in a speech before a bankers' convention and in a pamphlet he published. He proposed that banks pay a premium of 0.1 per cent a year on savings accounts into a central fund, which would insure savings accounts against loss, up to a limit of $10,000 per account. His scheme differed from the Federal deposit insurance program enacted by Congress in 1933 in two details only, the size of the annual insurance premium (the Federal premium is ½ per cent) and the management of the insurance fund. He had suggested that banks set up a bank-owned corporation to administer the fund. The Federal deposit insurance program is administered by a government corporation.

Another of Dr. W. E.'s interests was municipal affairs.

Around the turn of the century, he served as a member of the Kalamazoo City Council. Ten years later, while president of the Kalamazoo Chamber of Commerce, he became an advocate of the commission-manager form of city government (an elected mayor and commission or council to make municipal laws; a professional, nonpolitical city manager to direct police, fire, and other city departments). A campaign he organized led to the appointment of a committee—of which he was named chairman—to draft a new charter for Kalamazoo.

The charter committee's work, outlining a commission-manager form of government, went before the voters of Kalamazoo in 1918. It was carried by a large majority, and in the election that followed, Dr. W. E. was elected first mayor of Kalamazoo under its new form of government.

Dr. W. E. was also a firm believer in shorter hours of work. As a result, the Saturday half holiday was introduced at Upjohn in 1902—years before the Saturday half holiday had become standard in American industry and at a time when the Upjohn Company was not at all prosperous. Several years later, despite criticism from other Kalamazoo employers, he reduced the weekday hours of work in the Upjohn plant and office as well; and in 1915, stimulated by his son Harold, he introduced company-paid life insurance for all employees. It was one of the first industrial insurance plans in the United States to apply to both factory production and office workers and was the start of the comprehensive insurance program the Upjohn Company has developed over the years for its employees.

Through the years, Dr. W. E. made numerous and increasingly large gifts to institutions in and around Kalamazoo and to the city itself. He gave—often anonymously—to churches, hospitals, and welfare agencies and established the Kalamazoo Foundation for general philanthropic purposes. However, he had a special interest in the constructive use of the leisure time made possible by shorter hours of work. So, many of his gifts went to provide facilities and support for leisure-time activities: funds for building Kalamazoo's handsome Civic Auditorium and for supporting the symphony orchestra, little theater, and other activities housed in the auditorium; an art work center; a park; funds for improving two public golf courses.

Dr. W. E.'s own leisure-time pleasure was the raising of peonies. In 1895, he bought 40 acres of land from his mother-in-law, who had a farm near Augusta, a village east of Kalamazoo; soon, he rented and then bought another 40 acres of the farm. His first plan was to operate a creamery. When that proved unsuccessful, he remodeled the creamery and enlarged it into a seven-room summer home, which he named Brook Lodge after a stream crossing the property.

After his second marriage, Dr. W. E. gradually added to the acreage and the house and, with the aid of John De Young, his farmer, converted Brook Lodge into a handsome farm-estate. In addition, he set about raising flowers on it. His first choice was a stately Japanese iris. The soil proved unsuited for iris, however, so he switched to lilies, then poppies. He finally settled on peonies. At one time, he had 40 acres of peonies—698 varieties in all, and he wrote and had printed privately a book describing them.

Dr. Upjohn made it an invariable rule to be at Brook Lodge when the peonies bloomed. Although he was one of the first persons in Kalamazoo to own an automobile—first an Oldsmobile and then a White steamer that he regularly drove the few blocks to his office, though he had to get up at 6 A.M. to get the steamer fired up in time—he disliked travel. In his later years, he had a winter home in Pasadena, California. But he was prevailed upon to go abroad only once in his life. On that occasion, a trip to Europe with friends, he abruptly left the party halfway through the tour in order to be back in Kalamazoo in time to see the peonies bloom.

Dr. W. E. was never so happy as when at Brook Lodge. He so loved the farm and his flowers, his family recalls, that he literally shouted for joy when he arrived there. And it was at Brook Lodge that he died in the fall of 1932.

4 | Dr. W. E.'s "Big Thing"

One day in 1906, the "big thing" for which Dr. W. E. had been waiting and on which the Upjohn Company's further growth depended turned up—and was almost missed. It was a drug that made possible, for the first time, a pleasant-tasting laxative.

One morning, Frederick Childs, the man who had devised Caripeptic Liquid, handed Dr. Lawrence N. Upjohn—Dr. Henry U. Upjohn's son, who had joined the company in 1904—a bottle of white tablets. "Here's something new," Childs remarked, "a tasteless laxative. I wonder what's in it."

The tablets had been put out by a drug house in a neighboring state. Analysis showed them to contain phenolphthalein, a chemical reagent previously known in the United States only for the convenient property of turning red in the presence of bases and colorless in the presence of acids and therefore used as an acid-base indicator in chemical laboratories. No hint of other powers was contained in American technical or medical journals. German reports, however, said phenolphthalein was a cathartic; in Germany, a phenolphthalein laxative was also on the market.

Here was a prize sought by pharmaceutical houses for years—a laxative without an undisguisable, unpalatable taste. Actually, neither the German manufacturer nor the Middle Western company took real advantage of phenolphthalein's most striking feature; the simple, unflavored tablets they marketed never attained a big sale. At first, Upjohn started down the wrong track, too.

When the active ingredient of the tasteless laxative was finally identified, the first suggestion within the Upjohn Company was to add it to Upjohn's anticonstipation pill to make what would today have been called a "super-laxative" with "built-in multiple action" on the bowel. When a supply of phenolphthalein was obtained, Dr. James T. Upjohn prepared samples of just such a pill. He even had a name for it —Phenolax (though it is not clear who actually coined the name).

The new pill was brought to Dr. W. E.'s attention. The reaction of the head of the company was swift. He liked the name, in fact thought it was "too good for the product." He did not like combining phenolphthalein with other drugs in a compound pill. "Why not," he asked, "a flavored tablet to provide a pleasant-tasting laxative?" He immediately gave orders for the preparation of a flavored tablet containing phenolphthalein and no other cathartic ingredients. The result was the rectangular pink mint-flavored Phenolax wafer, incorporating 1 grain of phenolphthalein and scored for easy breaking in half, that soon became familiar from coast to coast, and that more than filled the void in the Upjohn position left by the decline of the friable pill.

Phenolax went on sale in 1908. Interestingly, Dr. W. E. was responsible not only for the basic idea of the flavored laxative; he later devised the machine for filling Phenolax bottles. Until then, pill and tablet bottles had been filled in most pharmaceutical plants with the aid of a machine that poured the pills and tablets through a funnel. The machine did not work with the rectangular Phenolax wafers; the wafers jammed in the funnel. Dr. W. E. worked out an ingenious arrangement—still utilized in many filling machines —for lining up the wafers and dropping them into the bottle one at a time.

Although Phenolax could be bought without a prescription, the new laxative was announced to physicians only, in accordance with Upjohn's policy as an ethical drug manufacturer. And it was put up chiefly in bottles of 500 and 1,000, sizes convenient to the druggist and dispensing physician. Only limited quantities were packed in bottles of 100 for direct sale to the public.

The Kalamazoo company's first inkling that it had struck a best-selling home medicament came within a few months. The plant ran out of no. 15 bottles, the size used for Phenolax 100s, though Dr. W. E.—who attended to the company's glassware ordering himself—had just laid in what he was sure was a full year's supply.

In order to introduce the new laxative, the company hit

upon a novel device that has since become a commonplace of pharmaceutical promotion. Postcard-sized sample cards containing an advertising message and ten Phenolax wafers under a strip of parchment were mailed to every physician in the United States. The hope was that the doctor would try the sample wafers himself or give them to a few patients and write prescriptions for more. Instead, doctors gave away entire cards and simply told patients to buy Phenolax as needed without a prescription. The mint flavor did the rest.

Sales of Phenolax grew without interruption until the outbreak of World War I cut off the German chemical industry, the world's source of phenolphthalein. Upjohn was able to keep Phenolax on the market throughout the war only because large stocks of phenolphthalein had been bought in anticipation of the war and because the company began packaging the laxatives in bottles of 30 instead of 100.

By the end of the war, several American companies were producing phenolphthalein. That brought both an opportunity and a problem. The opportunity was for a further increase in sales. The problem was the emergence of a host of competitors, ranging from other types of flavored laxative to outright imitations of Phenolax.

A number of expedients were employed in the effort to deal with imitators. The word *Phenolax* was imprinted on the wafers. Druggists were persuaded to post signs proclaiming, "No Substitutions in This Store—We Sell the Genuine Phenolax Wafers—In Original Bottles of 30." But the most effective measure by far was a bold departure from the policy of not advertising to the general public. For the first and one of the very few times in its history that it has done so, the Upjohn Company went directly to the public with a drugstore window display that outflanked the competition by making Phenolax a household word.

The display was built around "The Teeny Weenies," a favorite comic strip of the postwar period, and showed the Teeny Weeny elf men building a house of Phenolax building blocks. The display was suggested by Lewie M. Crockett, who later became Upjohn's vice-president of construction and engineering, and was executed by William Donehey, the cartoonist who created the Teeny Weenies. Drugstores ate up the display, which proved a crowd stopper, and called for more.

If there had been radio or TV comedians then, they would surely have worked Phenolax into their routines. As it was, it became part of the zany folklore of the 1920s. A North Carolina druggist constructed an elaborate display of Phenolax and offered a $5 gold piece and a bottle of 150 Phenolax tablets to the person who could write "Phenolax Wafers" the greatest number of times on a postcard. The winning card, with 1,727 renderings of the contest phrase on it, was sent to Kalamazoo and is now in the Upjohn files.) Doctors' sons dubbed their jalopies "Phenolax" instead of "Leaping Lena." An Upjohn salesman spotted a thoroughbred trotter named "Phenolax" (but never reported how well the horse made out).

The peak of Phenolax's popularity came in 1924, when 182,393,660 of the mint-flavored cathartic wafers were manufactured, and sales totaled $795,252 at the wholesale level, or 21 per cent of Upjohn's sales for the year. In earlier years, though their dollar volume was smaller, Phenolax sales accounted for an even larger proportion of over-all Upjohn sales—in some years, as high as 25 per cent.

In 1925, Phenolax sales began to slip, for (as Dr. W. E. once remarked) there are fashions in medicine as well as in women's hats. Other types of laxatives cut the Upjohn product's market. But Phenolax had dominated the highly competitive laxative field for a full decade and a half, and it continued to sell at a substantial, if declining, rate for over a quarter of a century more. In 1949, sales were still above the $100,000-a-year mark. In any event, when the decline began, other new products were already pressing forward to take the pink mint-flavored laxative's place as Upjohn's most successful product.

The success of Phenolax accomplished several essential purposes for Upjohn. One was to furnish funds for improvement of the company's laboratory facilities and enable a start on independent research, a story which will be told in later chapters. Another was to underwrite the expansion and reinforcement of the Upjohn sales organization.

In its early years, the Upjohn Company was represented by sales agencies in New York and Chicago and a handful of salesmen traveling mainly in the Middle West. The salesmen —of whom the first was a man named Booth, who was with Upjohn for a short time in 1887—were expected to be equally adept at detailing drugs to physicians and selling them to druggists. Some were outstanding personalities. Several, however, had little knowledge of drugs in general and only such knowledge of Upjohn's products in particular as could be imparted to them in last-minute coaching before they were sent on the road. Embarrassing episodes, consequently, were not unknown; thus, one new salesman took "friable" to mean "soluble" and told physicians they could make a cheap substitute for elixir of iron, quinine and strychnine by dissolving

Upjohn's friable iron, quinine and strychnine pills in water.

A major step toward the development of a more effective sales organization was taken in 1890, when a New York branch was set up under Frederick Upjohn. Further steps were the formal designation of a sales manager in 1904 and the bringing of Upjohn products to the Pacific Coast through an arrangement with an agent in San Francisco, Waters H. Sellman. Meanwhile the number of salesmen gradually increased.

In 1907, Frederick Upjohn fulfilled a long-held ambition to retire on his fiftieth birthday and sail on a voyage around the world. His successor as New York branch manager was Dr. Lawrence N. Upjohn. Dr. L. N. had obtained his medical degree from the family alma mater, the University of Michigan, then gone to the University of Oklahoma to teach a premedical anatomy course while Oklahoma organized a medical school (in which he was also to teach). After four years at Oklahoma, he accepted an invitation from Dr. W. E. to join the family enterprise. He served briefly in the assay laboratory, then in other posts (including a short term as sales manager) before going to New York.

As New York branch manager, Dr. L. N. brought about two basic changes that were to have far-reaching influence within the Upjohn Company. He put all salesmen working out of the New York office—which was responsible for sales throughout the Eastern United States—on straight salary instead of commission. Putting the salesmen on salary avoided the difficulty of computing commissions on orders from wholesale houses serving several sales territories. In addition, it ended the commission salesman's habit of pushing only best-selling items and enabled the company to choose what it wanted detailed.

Second, Dr. L. N. inaugurated the practice of holding sales conferences in which the features of Upjohn products were thoroughly discussed and uniform methods of selling developed. Both the salaried salesman and the sales conference are now standard throughout the company and have had no small part in the steady growth of Upjohn sales. Curiously, they were introduced by a man with no direct sales experience of his own. In his years with Upjohn, Dr. L. N. never detailed a physician or made a sales call on a drugstore.

The same period saw also a continued increase in the overall size of the sales force. In the course of time, Dr. L. N. had sixty salesmen working out of New York. George C. McClelland, who followed Dr. L. N. as sales manager in Kalamazoo after years as the company's star salesman, had a still larger number working out of the company headquarters. A Kansas City branch, with a sizable sales force of its own, was opened in 1909, and the San Francisco agency was enlarged and converted into a branch in 1911.

Finally, the Phenolax era witnessed the development of that indispensable tool of modern merchandising, market analysis. Under the influence of Dr. W. E.'s son Harold, who came into the company in 1907 and who had a strong interest in statistical analysis, a statistically minded employee was set to work analyzing the sales potential for different Upjohn products in different sales territories.

The expansion of the sales effort came in good time. In 1905, the American Medical Association set up the Council on Pharmacy and Chemistry to act as an authority on drugs. In order to clear the medical field of hundreds of drugs and drug mixtures of little or no value and pave the way to a more scientific approach to the treatment of disease, the council adopted a series of rigorous rules regarding trademarked mixtures of standard drugs especially. The action hit many pharmaceutical companies, Upjohn among them. Upjohn felt that it could not change its trademark policy to conform with the council's new rules. Since only council-approved products could be advertised in A.M.A. publications, the advertising pages of the *Journal of the American Medical Association* and other A.M.A. journals were closed to the Kalamazoo firm. Upjohn finally sought and obtained council acceptance for Upjohn products in 1937.

In retrospect, the council's action was an essential step toward modern drug therapy. But for many years, it greatly reduced the use of medical journal advertising by Upjohn and put the growth of the company—whose researchers were to develop many of the new kind of drugs the council sought —squarely up to the salesmen calling on the doctor and druggist.

Between 1887 and 1909, Dr. W. E. and his two younger brothers continued in the corporate offices to which they had been elected in 1887. In 1909, however, Dr. W. E. purchased the stock owned by Frederick and Dr. James. As a result, for many years afterward, Dr. W. E. owned or controlled almost all the stock in the company. Thereafter, neither Frederick (who had already retired from the New York office) nor Dr. James had any connection with the Upjohn Company. Frederick devoted himself to other interests when he returned from his round-the-world trip. Dr. James practiced medicine and then entered the Michigan state legislature, in which he served, first as a representative, then as a senator, until his death.

5 | Beginning of Upjohn Research

In 1906, the Congress of the United States enacted a law designed to curb abuses in the manufacture and sale of food and drugs. The new Pure Food and Drugs Act was received by the pharmaceutical industry with reactions varying from apprehension to outright opposition. Patent medicine manufacturers were vehemently opposed; the law's limitations upon label claims and the requirement that alcohol, opiates, and similar ingredients be disclosed on the label drove scores of secret-formula nostrums off the market. Responsible ethical drug manufacturers, such as Dr. W. E. Upjohn, were fearful that the new law would bring harassment by bribe-seeking inspectors.

As a matter of fact, many ethical drug firms did have

brushes with the new law, sometimes through sheer inadvertence. In 1911, for instance, as a result of a long-held interest by Dr. W. E. in entering the food or candy business, the Upjohn Company attempted to market a mint candy called Kazoo Mints. To everyone's surprise, the company was soon embroiled in charges of food adulteration. No one in Upjohn knew that starch—long used as a binder in molding drug tablets and still widely used for that purpose—may not be employed in molding candies; in candy, starch is classed as an adulterant. The Kazoo Mints were abandoned forthwith.

A more serious difficulty was the problem of specified dosage. In 1907, when the new law went into effect, the pharmaceutical industry did not know how to produce a 5-grain tablet that could be relied on to contain 5 grains of medication; the tablet was as apt to contain 4 or 6 grains as five. Uniform preparations of nitroglycerin (utilized in treating heart disease) were likewise hard to produce because of nitroglycerin's volatility; nearly all contained either too little nitroglycerin or too much. Under the Food and Drugs Act, such variations from the potency printed on the label made drugs subject to seizure for misbranding.

The Upjohn Company dealt with the problem in a way that was to have far-reaching results. A chemist—Upjohn's first scientist with a Ph.D. degree—was hired to work out improved methods of assaying drugs and controlling production. As happened also in a number of other pharmaceutical houses beside Upjohn, once the chemist and his aides had the control task in hand, they moved inevitably on to the investigation of new products, and then into independent research. Thus, in Upjohn and several other firms, organized pharmaceutical research got its start.

The chemist hired by Upjohn was Frederick William Heyl (pronounced "Hile"), a young man who had obtained his degree at his home town university (Yale) and been professor of chemistry at the University of Wyoming. Dr. Heyl came to Upjohn in 1913. He was employed by Dr. S. Rudolph Light, who had succeeded Dr. James Upjohn as production manager and who served as production manager until 1930. Dr. Light, a son-in-law of Dr. W. E. (husband of Dr. W. E.'s daughter Winifred), was one of the first in the company to realize that professional chemists were needed to do away with the rule-of-thumb methods still used in many areas of pharmaceutical manufacturing.

One day, while Dr. Heyl was setting up the control laboratory, Dr. W. E. remarked to William F. Little, head of the tablet department, "This is going to cost me $50,000, and I don't know where the money is coming from."

Dr. Heyl's laboratory and staff eventually cost far more than $50,000—and more than repaid the larger sum. Before joining Upjohn, the young chemist (he was twenty-eight at the time he came to Kalamazoo) had also worked in the Federal government's Chicago food and drug laboratory. As a result, he was thoroughly acquainted with the type of assay needed to meet the drug law's requirements. In addition, he and his first aides—Dr. Merrill C. Hart (who later became an Upjohn vice-president and research director) and J. Fred Staley—quickly became involved in activities ranging from the preparation of technical bulletins on Upjohn products for physicians and the sales force to research on production processes and new products. And his title was soon changed from chief chemist to director of the research division.

Dr. Heyl's laboratory was in the basement of the "White Office," a handsome though, by present standards, small **new** headquarters office building; Dr. W. E.'s desk was almost directly overhead on the floor above. From the basement laboratory (which Dr. Heyl occupied for twenty-two years) came the first research paper from the Upjohn laboratories —"Notes on the Estimation of Nitroglycerine" by F. W. Heyl and J. F. Staley, in the *American Journal of Pharmacy* for May, 1914. From the basement laboratory, too, came the first major development of Upjohn research—Digitora, Upjohn's dated, protected-against-deterioration oral digitalis tablet.

One of the very few drugs which can be described as both old and therapeutically potent is digitalis, the dried powdered leaf of *Digitalis purpurea*, the common foxglove of garden and field. Mentions of digitalis are to be found in medical literature as far back as 1000 A.D. Its regular use in medicine goes back to Dr. William Withering of Birmingham, England. In 1775, Withering obtained the recipe for a tea brewed from twenty or more herbs with which an old woman in his neighborhood had been treating dropsy with considerable success. In *Account of the Foxglove* (published 1785), Withering announced that digitalis was the herb responsible for the beneficial effect of the tea and described the use of foxglove leaves in over two hundred cases of dropsy.

Digitalis relieves "dropsy"—the abnormal accumulation of fluid about the ankles and in other parts of the body, generally as a result of heart disease—through its action on the heart. Digitalis increases the pumping efficiency of the heart by increasing the force of the heart's contractions and also, in patients whose hearts are beating too rapidly, by slowing the beat. It can keep a failing heart going for many months or even years and is universally used today for treating many forms of heart failure. Physicians invariably list it as one of the half-dozen indispensable drugs to be taken with them on the proverbial trip to a desert island. No substitute for digitalis or its derivatives or a closely related heart drug from another plant, ouabain, has ever been found.

In the early years of the twentieth century, however, digitalis was in bad repute. The foxglove medicine is not easy to use in any event. The medical dose is nearly equal to the toxic dose, and the drug accumulates unpredictably in the body. A dose that maintains a patient beautifully one month can cause marked signs of poisoning the next, and it may have little useful effect on the heart of a second, seemingly comparable patient. Two generations ago, the physician not only had to contend with these difficulties (which still apply to digitalis and its derivatives); the digitalis preparations then available were bewilderingly variable in potency, and methods of assaying the foxglove drug were in dispute.

Dr. Heyl began work on the digitalis problem shortly after his arrival in Kalamazoo. At that time, the most widely utilized type of digitalis preparation was a tincture prepared from the whole powdered leaf. Several firms were marketing tinctures which were claimed to be stable. Careful analysis by Dr. Heyl showed, though, that "stability" had been achieved by merely allowing the tincture to deteriorate before it was placed on sale so that little further deterioration was to be expected. Tincture of digitalis kept on the shelf for a year or so, Upjohn's first graduate chemist found, loses about 60 per cent of its initial activity and thereafter remains more or less at constant strength.

In subsequent experiments, Dr. Heyl traced the deterioration to decomposition of all but one of the several active substances present in the original digitalis leaf. Nearly always, the final strength of the tincture was almost equal to the initial concentration of digitoxin, the single decomposition-resistant active component of the leaf.

In recent years, purified digitoxin has been prescribed by physicians more often than whole digitalis; modern pharmacology has shown that the desired effects of whole digitalis on the heart can be achieved with digitoxin alone. But in those years, this was far from clear. Medical opinion held that it was necessary to give whole digitalis in order to obtain the full effects of the foxglove drug.

A number of physicians recommended that commercial tinctures be avoided and that doctors either give the patient whole powdered leaf in tablet form or prepare their own fresh infusions as needed. But that involved difficulties, too. For dry digitalis leaf preparations were likewise highly variable in potency and, as Dr. Heyl found in the laboratory, also subject to deterioration.

Close study showed that the deterioration of the various preparations of whole digitalis was due chiefly to the effects of light and moisture. Dr. Heyl accordingly devised a dark, sealed container with a built-in desiccator. Packed in this way, dry powdered digitalis can be guaranteed to keep virtually its original potency for several years.

The Upjohn Company's original intention was to utilize Dr. Heyl's novel method of packaging the foxglove drug—for which the chemist received a patent—for a large tablet, prepared from carefully assayed, rigidly standardized powdered leaf, with which the physician would make his own infusion. But when the infusion tablets were shown to a prominent heart specialist, he asked, "Why don't you simply make this in the form of an oral tablet and let the man's belly make the infusion?" Both types of tablet were therefore put on the market—a large infusion tablet, guaranteed stable and dated for good measure, trademarked Diginfuse; and a smaller oral tablet, also dated and warranted stable, named Digitora.

The two new digitalis preparations were placed on sale in 1919, nearly five years after Dr. Heyl had gone to work on the digitalis problem. The infusion tablet did not meet a good response because the oral tablet was, as the heart specialist had predicted, equally effective and was in fact simpler to use; hence, Diginfuse was soon dropped. But Digitora was taken up by many physicians, especially in the great school of cardiology that was growing up around the Boston medical schools. Digitora became and remained one of Upjohn's most important products, both in terms of its lifesaving value to patients and physicians and in terms of sales, through World War II, when digitoxin and other purified-principle preparations finally outstripped whole digitalis as the doctor's choice in treating the failing heart.

In order to keep members of the research department and other key personnel abreast of new developments in medicine and related fields, pharmaceutical houses today maintain extensive libraries, especially of scientific and medical journals. Many subscribe to literally hundreds of journals and some, such as Upjohn, even go to the expense of preparing brief abstracts of important papers to call them to the attention of staff members.

Two generations ago, pharmaceutical houses had no such machinery for keeping track of new trends in medicine. The physicians on the Upjohn staff—L. N. Upjohn in New York and S. R. Light and Eugene Caldwell in Kalamazoo—followed the medical journals. But lack of time limited their journal reading mainly to periodicals in the field of pharmacology and therapeutics. Journals in other fields, such as physiology, were not regularly read. One day in 1914, however, a star salesman, Montague Pollock, who served the New York branch as detailer and who selected and trained many of Upjohn's most successful salesmen, reported to Dr. L. N. Upjohn, "Doctors are interested in alkalis." They were in fact prescribing them in large quantities.

Pollock was mystified, and so was Dr. Upjohn, the more so since at about the same time another salesman reported that surgeons were giving patients alkalis before anesthesia. Alkaline salts, such as sodium bicarbonate, had been used for many years to neutralize stomach acidity; but this was something new, for physicians were giving them for other types of illness and for some sort of systemic effect on the body as a whole and not a local effect upon the digestive system.

What neither Pollock nor Dr. Upjohn—nor, for that matter, anyone else in the pharmaceutical industry—knew was that a major medical discovery was just then emerging from new studies of blood. This was that blood is normally slightly alkaline but that changes in its acid-base balance may occur during illness, with serious consequences for the patient.

The alkalinity of blood was one of many discoveries made by researchers inspired by a profound truth about life first enunciated in 1855 by Claude Bernard of France. Bernard had come to Paris to write plays; he stayed to become the founder of modern physiology and the first man of science

Donald S. Gilmore. Elected president and general manager 1943; chairman of the board and managing director 1952.

E. Gifford Upjohn, M.D. Elected president in 1952.

Mechanical equipment a[ids]
the chemist. This machine [in]
continuous operation equ[als]
a thousand men shaking [a]
thousand test tubes.

The detection of new age[nts]
for the treatment of dise[ase]
is an important part of t[he]
work of people in microbi[ol-]
ogy.

Medical research is dependent on the ability to measure and record. This recording
equipment is in the behavior laboratory of
Upjohn's pharmacology department.

ever accorded a public funeral in France. Bernard's great discovery was that life depends on the maintenance of a constant internal environment. For instance (as Bernard himself discovered), the amount of sugar in human blood normally varies only within fairly narrow limits; as fast as blood sugar is taken up by the tissues and used for fuel, it is replaced by the liver. Death or illness results if the concentration of blood sugar goes too high or too low.

Around 1900, physiological researchers began to find a host of other mechanisms by which the body preserves its exquisite internal balance. One involves the blood. The latter is ordinarily just barely alkaline, and the body has an assortment of powerful mechanisms for keeping it that way. Suppose the blood begins to shift away from normal because of an excess of some substance, acid or alkaline; numerous mechanisms swiftly come into play to remove the excess or to release neutralizing agents and so restore blood to its normal slightly alkaline state.

In illnesses accompanied by damage to body tissues, though, the body's acid-base "buffering" mechanism may be strained or even overwhelmed; the blood may then become less alkaline and more acid than usual. This may also occur as a result of injury and during anesthesia or surgery. A different and very dangerous form of acidosis may develop in diabetes.

Physicians of the World War I era had only limited knowledge of the damage acidosis can do, of the interference with the flow of oxygen to, and carbon dioxide away from, the tissues, and the other internal derangements to which acidosis may lead. They knew merely that it occurred in many of the illnesses they were called on to treat and that it could lead to excessive elimination of salt and water from the body and thus dehydrate the patient. They felt that disturbing departure from the normal ought, if possible, to be reversed. They set out to treat it by the simple expedient of administering large doses of the familiar antacid, sodium bicarbonate, and other alkaline salts—sometimes at a rate of several ounces a day. They found that such antacid salts corrected the patient's dehydration.

The talk Pollock had heard related to this use of "systemic alkalizers." Although neither Pollock nor Dr. L. N. Upjohn yet knew why physicians were suddenly interested in alkalizers, they were aware of something else: that large doses of sodium bicarbonate are hard to take. The result was an impromptu experiment in the New York office. The branch had in its stock a few bottles of artificial Vichy salts —a popular aid to dieting—composed mainly of magnesium citrate and other salts that are converted to alkaline compounds in the body. Dr. L. N. mixed the artificial Vichy salts with sodium bicarbonate to see whether the latter's unpleasant taste could be disguised.

The experiment did not convince Dr. W. E., who was persuaded to sample the concoction during a visit to the New York office. Dr. L. N. took up with Dr. Heyl the possibility of preparing a more palatable systemic alkalizer to meet what he saw as a sizable potential demand.

At first, Dr. L. N.'s proposal received scant attention from the research laboratory. World War I was on, and the first concern of the entire Upjohn Company was preservation of the phenolphthalein supply in order to save the Phenolax business. In addition, Dr. Heyl was fully occupied with drug-assay and production-control problems and with his research on digitalis. But Dr. Heyl did find time, along with Dr. L. N., to conduct a thorough canvass of recent blood-chemistry literature and learn the reason for the medical world's interest in alkalizers; and small lots of experimental alkalizing combinations were prepared.

A product acceptable to the taste was finally ready for sale in 1921. It was an effervescent mixture of bicarbonates, citrates, tartrates, and other alkalizing salts of the four principal alkaline bases found in blood plasma—sodium, potassium, magnesium, and calcium—in the proportions in which they are present in plasma and other intercellular body fluids. The mixture was packed as an effervescent granular salt named Citrocarbonate.

When the new Upjohn product was introduced, a respectable but not large market was anticipated for it. For one thing, some of the ingredients were high in cost and uncertain as to supply. For another, the mixture was not easily stabilized; as originally prepared, the salts had an unhappy tendency to react in the bottle. For a third, the hand-blown glass bottles in which it was first packed were expensive.

The several difficulties were gradually overcome; the bottle problem by the fortuitous development of automatic bottle-blowing machinery by the glass industry shortly after World War I. Thus the cost of Citrocarbonate was brought down. The effervescent alkalizer thereupon caught hold. In 1923, sales of Citrocarbonate totaled $420,000, or roughly one-eighth of the Upjohn Company's entire business for the year. In 1925, Citrocarbonate passed Phenolax as Upjohn's biggest seller and, in 1926, became the first Upjohn product to achieve a volume of more than $1 million a year. By 1931, Citrocarbonate sales reached $2,081,000 a year (the peak) and accounted for 25.4 per cent of Upjohn sales. Twenty years later, the effervescent salt was still selling at a rate of over $1 million a year.

Citrocarbonate won a prominent place in four distinct areas of medicine. One was in the treatment of infectious illnesses, especially illnesses marked by fever, acidosis, and dehydration. In 1914, only a few physicians—chiefly in and around New York, an early center of blood-chemistry research—had really been aware that such illnesses are frequently accompanied by acidosis; by 1921, the knowledge was spreading throughout the country. Another application of Citrocarbonate was in surgical anesthesia; surgeons prescribed it before operations under the slogan, "preoperative alkalinization for postoperative comfort."

Perhaps the most popular use of Citrocarbonate was as a gastric antacid. The effervescent salt was an easy-to-take neutralizer of stomach acidity. Finally, on the strength of claims by a number of physicians, Citrocarbonate even had a vogue as a cold preventive.

The success of Citrocarbonate led to several variations on the Citrocarbonate theme by Upjohn, and to numerous imitations by others. Among the former were Bromionyl (an effervescent alkalizer-sedative bromide preparation, designed to avoid the stomach irritation often caused by bromides) and Salicionyl (a similar preparation of sodium salicylate, a pain reliever akin to aspirin); both proved popular. Not so fortunate was Upjohn's Acetonyl, an effervescent alkalizer-aspirin combination for headache and simple pain. Acetonyl lost the sales contest to a similar product put out by a proprietary house and, unlike Acetonyl, heavily advertised to the public.

Today, systemic alkalizers, such as Citrocarbonate, no longer hold the position they once had. But their decline in importance has not been owing to any rejection of the fundamental idea of acid-base balance and its relationship to salt and water balance and the patient's well-being. Physicians still keep a sharp eye on acid-base balance, as well as on many other aspects of blood chemistry of which little was known thirty years ago. What has changed is the approach. Physicians now know better when alterations in the blood are trivial and can be ignored (as they can be in most illnesses); in other illnesses and in surgical operations, treatment is designed to prevent harmful blood-chemistry alterations from taking place or to deal with the specific causes of those that do occur. Systemic alkalizers are little used nowadays only because medicine has other, more effective methods of coping with the balance of salts in the blood.

Like the United States pharmaceutical industry as a whole, by the mid-1920s the Upjohn Company had begun to assume its modern form. The family partnership launched four decades before by the friable pill had grown into an enterprise with some 800 employees and a gross business of more than $4 million a year. It had a sizable group of plant buildings and a varied list of products that included several still familiar today. An active, if small, research laboratory and other distinguishing features of the modern pharmaceutical manufacturer had made their appearance. A number of the men who were to play a prominent part in building Upjohn in the 1940s and 1950s—such as W. Fred Allen, future vice-president for marketing, and C. V. Patterson, future executive vice-president—were already on the scene.

Moreover, the outline of the great trapezoid-shaped complex of buildings Upjohn now occupies in downtown Kalamazoo was clearly visible. A half-dozen massive red brick buildings, built over the years, stretched from Portage Street to Lovell Street. In front, set well back on an elm-shaded lawn extending to Henrietta Street and dwarfed by the plant buildings behind it, stood the White Office. At Henrietta and Lovell, stood an old house later used as a temporary office. Missing still, however, were two of today's most conspicuous landmarks: the downtown administration building (Building 24) and the Research Tower (Building 25), Kalamazoo's tallest structure.

The White Office was built in 1913 to the design of W. Harold Upjohn—Dr. W. E.'s son—and L. M. Crockett, the company's construction and engineering superintendent. It was quite a departure from the usual manufacturing-plant office building. It was square, one high-ceilinged story tall, and had large expanses of glass. Four white Doric columns across the front, surmounted by a band of molding, gave it a name and a colonial mien. A flat-topped sloping red tile roof heightened the effect. Inside, a plant-filled solarium was attached to Dr. W. E.'s office.

When the White Office was erected, it was expected to have both a long and a useful life. Its career was useful—it housed Upjohn's first research laboratory and served as a center for Upjohn guests as well as a company office—but not long. By 1925, as a result of Upjohn's steady growth, it was already becoming overcrowded. In 1934–1935, its place as home office was taken by Building 24 and it was torn down to make way for the Research Tower.

By the mid-1920s, Upjohn had not only a research laboratory and a production-control staff but also a biological laboratory. The latter had been set up in 1914. Its functions included all types of biological testing and investigation. Its activities were centered chiefly, however, around bacteriology and the numerous applications of bacteriology to the manufacture of pharmaceuticals. One problem was the proper handling of medicines—especially fluid medicines, which spoil more easily than dry preparations—during and after manufacture to prevent bacterial spoilage. Another was the development of sterile medications for injection, an undertaking entailing the solution of many special problems, such as the filtering of large volumes of fluid under sterile conditions, aseptic filling of vials and other containers, and sterility tests of the final products. Still another task of the biological laboratory was the development of vaccines, an assignment involving not only all the problems of preparing sterile solutions for injection but the additional problems of culturing microbes.

As a result of these varied activities, Upjohn now had a broad line of products. The catalogue listed not only numerous long-familiar items and the popular Phenolax wafers and the two new stars, Digitora and Citrocarbonate. It included more than a dozen sterile injectable drugs in several dosage forms (added to the Upjohn list beginning in 1917) and a line of vaccines (added beginning in 1921), including typhoid, influenza, whooping cough, and pneumococcal and streptococcal vaccines. (Upjohn never became a major factor in the vaccine field, however, and in 1950 withdrew from it completely.)

Also in the catalogue by 1924 was a product, the cough medicine Cheracol, that was to give Upjohn both an embarrassing moment and one of its outstanding successes. Like other effective cough remedies of the time, the Cheracol formula included morphine as the active cough-suppressing agent. Not long after the Cheracol morphine compound was introduced, a number of unscrupulous druggists on the West Coast began selling it to narcotic addicts for its morphine content. Upjohn hastily substituted codeine for the morphine. The codeine proved effective enough as a cough suppressant, the tart taste of the syrup proved popular, and Cheracol with codeine went on to become a household standby—a position it occupies to this day.

In the early days of the Upjohn Company, the cost of the products sold was figured by an extremely simple and crude system. The manufacturing cost of pills, for example, was calculated by taking the total material and labor cost for the pill department and dividing by the number of pills produced. Thus, all pills had the same nominal cost, whatever their size or content. No allocation of light or power, administrative, or other overhead costs was made. Nor was there any effort to determine the cost of selling—the price of the salesman's time, the cost of the advertising, and other promotion activities—for any particular product. As a consequence, products were sometimes sold at, or even well below, their real cost.

Dr. W. E. recognized that this was no way to do business. Accordingly, by 1904, he had inaugurated a novel dual system of calculating costs. Estimates were made of the share of each department in the company's over-all administrative costs.

These allowances were then distributed over batch lots of the various types of products and added to material and labor costs—now also calculated on an individual-lot basis—to arrive at a manufactured cost for each batch of products made. Simultaneously, the factory cost of each item sold was entered on each order.

The system was not to be compared with present cost-accounting methods. But the figures enabled Dr. W. E. to spot grossly unprofitable sales and to distinguish between salesmen who were making profitable sales and those who were not.

The "sales-costing" scheme was an invaluable aid to the growth of the company. Moreover, along with the batch-costing scheme, it laid the basis for the gradual development, over the next several decades, of a comprehensive cost-accounting system. By the mid-1920s, the main lines of the system had been laid down; and Upjohn was playing a leading role in the preparation, through the American Drug Manufacturers' Association, of a pioneer cost manual for the drug industry as a whole.

Sales methods had become more sophisticated, too. In 1923, Malcolm Galbraith, who had organized and been sales manager of the Kansas City branch, came to Kalamazoo as sales manager for the Kalamazoo area and *de facto* sales manager for the entire company. Under Galbraith's vigorous direction, the occasional sales conferences of previous years quickly became a regular part of the Upjohn salesmen's routine. In addition, new members of the constantly growing sales staff—the company had 208 salesmen in 1925—were put through a systematic course of training before being sent out to call on druggists and physicians. And branch managers began keeping the comparative territory-by-territory sales records by which the company today keeps track of how it is doing and where it might be doing better. The Upjohn Company was far from the large, highly organized producer and distributor of pharmaceuticals it would become, but it was on the way.

6 | Vitamin Venture

One of the central factors in the development of modern medicine and the modern pharmaceutical industry was the discovery of vitamins. They form a key factor in the history of the Upjohn Company, too. Vitamins contributed greatly to the company's growth; and research at Upjohn played a significant part in making vitamin food supplements a common household article.

The product that brought Upjohn (and numerous other pharmaceutical houses) into the nutritional supplement field was cod liver oil. Cod liver oil's most important constituent is vitamin D, one of the so-called fat-soluble vitamins. Several other vitamins were discovered before D. Wide use of vitamin supplements began, however, with the discovery of vitamin

D's remarkable power to prevent rickets, the disease that bends bones.

During much of the eighteenth and nineteenth centuries, cod liver oil was widely regarded as having valuable medicinal properties. It enjoyed a brief vogue as a remedy for tuberculosis. There were even physicians who prescribed it for rickets (whose name is derived from *wrikken,* an old English word meaning to bend or twist), though nothing was known of vitamins or of the nature of rickets as a vitamin-deficiency disease.

Most nineteenth-century thinkers believed that rickets was caused by overcrowding. In the late 1930s—by which time authentic knowledge of how to prevent rickets was widespread—X-ray studies revealed at least minimal signs of the disease in over 25 per cent of United States children. In the nineteenth century, nearly all children must have had some degree of rachitic bone damage, and severe rickets was frequent, especially in sunless, overcrowded northern cities. It was entirely natural for the reformers who fought the appalling slums of the nineteenth-century factory town to add rickets to the roster of ills blamed on overcrowding.

Opinion did not begin to change until 1889, when an English physician, Sir John Bland-Sutton, published the results of an attention-catching investigation into the health of animals in the London Zoo. Sir John found bone defects very common in nearly all species, and particularly among lion cubs raised on lean meat. He suggested adding crushed bones and cod liver oil to the cubs' diet. His suggestion gave the London Zoo the first healthy lions ever reared in captivity and planted the idea that rickets might be the result of a defect in diet—a defect that could be remedied with cod liver oil.

Thirty years later, another English investigator, the nutritionist Sir Edward Mellanby, carried out a series of experiments conclusively proving rickets a dietary deficiency disease. Mellanby raised groups of puppies—all housed under excellent laboratory conditions—on four different dietary regimens. All four diets were wholly composed of natural foods. Two contained a modest ration of whole milk, known from research completed only a few years before to provide vitamin A, a vitamin essential to growth as well as night vision; two contained yeast, which would be described today as a source of B vitamins. All four diets nevertheless produced rickets.

Mellanby also found that he could prevent rickets by adding a number of different supplementary food substances to the puppies' rations. Of these, cod liver oil was by far the most effective. But Mellanby was unable to pinpoint the agent in cod liver oil responsible for the antirachitic effect. That remained for biochemist E. V. McCollum and his associates at Johns Hopkins University. In 1922, Dr. McCollum and his colleagues showed that cod liver oil contains a vitamin distinct from vitamin A (which is also present in cod liver oil and other fish liver oils) and that this new vitamin, which they named vitamin D, is the antirachitic substance.

As a result of the Mellanby and McCollum discoveries, several pharmaceutical houses began marketing cod liver oil preparations as an antirachitic for infants and children. Upjohn likewise decided to add the fish liver oil to its line. Cod liver oil promised to be not only a highly useful product but one with a substantial market potential. Not long before, the Food and Drug Administration had created something of a vacuum in popular medicinals by banning the labeling and sale of many old-time medicines (such as "iron and strychnine tonic") as "tonics" on the ground that they had no real tonic effect on health. Cod liver oil provided a product with a specific health-promoting function that could be offered to, and by, physicians as an alternate to the nondescript tonics outlawed by the FDA.

In 1927, Upjohn marketed a flavored cod liver oil, essentially similar to many competing preparations. The company determined, however, to try to apply to cod liver oil, as to other of its most successful products, two of the chief lessons learned in forty years of pharmaceutical manufacturing. One was to make its product a specialty sufficiently superior and distinctive to stand out from competing products. The other was to furnish the physician, in any event, with what is wanted in any medicinal product—a preparation with a known, standardized content of active ingredients.

Most of the cod liver oils then on the market varied widely from bottle to bottle in vitamin content as well as in taste and odor. This was owing in part to variations in the oil derived from different lots of fish and to variations in storing and handling; in part, it was also due to the newness and unfamiliarity of the procedures required for assaying vitamin potency. The vitamin D content—the critical constituent of the oil, since vitamin A could be obtained from other sources —was particularly unpredictable. It could vary by as much 1,000 per cent from one lot of oil to the next.

To develop a superior cod liver oil product, the Upjohn Company added a small nutrition laboratory to its research department. At its head, Dr. Heyl, the research director, placed Edwin C. Wise, a chemist who had just joined the company. Wise, who soon acquired a reputation as an encyclopedic reader of scientific literature as well as an able investigator, remained in charge of the nutrition laboratory (which was expanded many times) until his death in 1947.

Wise's first step was to adapt elaborate animal tests for vitamin potency, used previously only in the research laboratory, to use as routine control procedures. With their aid, the nutrition laboratory was able to select vitamin-rich lots of oil for processing into a cod liver oil standardized as to both vitamin A and D potency. This was Super D cod liver oil, introduced in 1928, the first standardized A-and-D vitamin product to gain national recognition.

Super D cod liver oil enjoyed steadily increasing popularity as a pediatric nutritional supplement for several years, until competitors brought out highly concentrated preparations that provided the daily vitamin D dose in a few drops instead of a teaspoonful. These were prepared in either of two ways. Several utilized fish liver oils of species, such as the halibut and percomorph, with considerably higher vitamin D content than the cod. Others were based on one of the most celebrated discoveries of the 1920s, the Steenbock irradiation process.

Among the circumstances that had obscured the dietary origin of rickets was the fact that rickets is uncommon in warm, sunny climates, where children wear little clothing and play outdoors all year. The unraveling of the no-rickets-in-sunshine puzzle began in Dr. McCollum's laboratory at Hopkins in 1921, with the discovery that four hours of summer sunshine daily would protect young rats against the worst effects of a rickets-producing diet (though not so well as a dose of cod liver oil). The next year, Dr. E. M. Hume of England found that exposure to ultraviolet rays had the same effect. Soon afterward, ultraviolet rays were found by a num-

ber of investigators to form vitamin D in the livers of rats on
rickets-producing diets; and Dr. Harry Steenbock and his
associates at the University of Wisconsin discovered that
irradiation will also form the "sunshine vitamin" in many
foods. Dr. Steenbock particularly found that a concentrated
preparation of the vitamin is easily formed by irradiating
ergosterol, a fatlike substance found in many plants.

Upjohn attempted to obtain a license to produce irradiated
ergosterol by the Steenbock process, which Dr. Steenbock
had patented. But the Wisconsin Alumni Research Foundation, to which Dr. Steenbock had assigned his patents, was
then following a limited licensing policy; since Upjohn was
not among the early applicants, its request for a license was
refused. It was evident that the Kalamazoo company would
have to find another method of producing drop-dosage vitamin D if it meant to stay in the vitamin business.

One expedient tried was the irradiation of ergosterol by
natural sunlight, which, of course, was not covered by the
Steenbock patents. Land was rented in a sunny area of the
Southwest, and large trays of ergosterol set out. Vitamin D
was produced, but the capital investment and handling costs
proved prohibitive.

Another possible approach was the discovery of some
means of raising the potency of Super D cod liver oil. In
the course of selecting oils for processing into the Super D
product, Wise and his aides in the nutrition laboratory had
studied the vitamin A and D content, taste, odor, and other
characteristics of cod liver oils from all the world's principal
production centers. Some samples, obtained through Norwe-
gian fish oil brokers, were found to have an unusually high
vitamin D content—as much as 500 international units per

gram, a potency nearly comparable to that of haliver and percomorph oil.

In 1936, Wise went to Norway to track down the extra-potent oil. Careful diplomatic maneuvering—the brokers were not anxious to give up the secret of their top-grade oil —disclosed Iceland as the source of the prized lots of oil. Wise then went to Iceland to see if he could determine the origin of the oil more precisely, for only some lots of oil from the mid-Atlantic island were of the top grade.

Wise spent half a year in Iceland. He set up a laboratory —test animals and all—for assaying the vitamin content of oils produced on various types of fishing vessels from various of the Icelandic fishing grounds at different times of the year. The extra-potent oil was found to come from cod caught at a fishing ground off the Iceland north coast during two months each fall. Wise returned home after laboratory tests in Kalamazoo confirmed his findings and after he had arranged for a regular supply of the extra-rich oil and had trained Icelanders to continue the assay tests by which the extra-rich oil was identified.

The Upjohn Company now had one prerequisite for a thoroughly competitive vitamin D product—an unusually potent cod liver oil. A second came through a development by a pharmaceutical firm in New York, the International Vitamin Corporation. The New York firm's laboratory found a solvent, an organic chemical called ethylene dichloride, that dissolved vitamin D and could be used to extract and concentrate vitamin D from cod liver oil. Upjohn was able to obtain an exclusive United States license to the concentration process.

The Upjohn nutrition laboratory utilized the concentra-

tion process to produce from the extra-rich Iceland cod liver
oil vitamin A and D concentrates suitable for preparing
capsules or for drop dosage. Thus the Kalamazoo company
was once more in a thoroughly competitive position in the
vitamin field. More than that: Super D concentrate capsules
and the liquid concentrate—as manufactured after 1934—
were therapeutically more effective than equivalent dosages
of irradiated ergosterol. Shortly after the development of the
ergosterol irradiation process, it was found that ultraviolet
treatment of the plant sterol leads to a form of vitamin D
known as D_2, rather than the vitamin D_3 occurring in cod
liver oil. Further study, by Dr. Donald J. Barnes and associates of the Detroit Department of Health and others, revealed that vitamin D_2 is less than half as effective as vitamin
D_3, unit for unit, in preventing rickets and promoting normal bone growth in human beings.

Both before and after the years of research that brought
the discovery of the fat-soluble vitamins A and D, medical
scientists in several countries carried out dietary and other
experiments that led to the identification of numerous additional vitamins, which became known as the B vitamins.
These differed from vitamins A and D in being soluble in
water. As was to be expected, as each new vitamin was identified and shown to be essential in human nutrition, pharmaceutical manufacturers sought to add it to their vitamin
preparations. At Upjohn, the process led to the development
of one of the most successful products in the company's history—Unicap multivitamin capsules.

The full story of the discovery of the B vitamins can
hardly be told, even in specialized histories of nutrition re-

search. Many investigators had a hand in tracking them down. During the 1930s especially, discoveries came thick and fast.

Briefly, in 1925—some years after B vitamin was first shown to be essential to nutrition—U.S. Public Health Service researchers obtained conclusive evidence that vitamin B was not one substance, but two and perhaps more. The first, vitamin B_1, or thiamine, the antiberiberi factor, was finally isolated in pure form in 1935 by Dr. Robert R. Williams, director of chemical research at Bell Telephone Laboratories, who carried on vitamin research in his spare time. A year later, Dr. Williams and several colleagues worked out a method of synthesizing thiamine.

Vitamin B_2, or riboflavin, an essential of normal growth, was isolated by Dr. Harry C. Sherman of Columbia University in 1931. Two years later, its synthesis was achieved, independently and almost simultaneously, by Swiss and German chemists. The 1930s saw also the final establishment of niacin, or nicotinic acid, as the pellagra-preventive factor discovered by Dr. Joseph Goldberger of the Public Health Service and others in 1926.

In addition, pyridoxine, or vitamin B_6—required for normal neurological development in infants—was first demonstrated in 1934, isolated in 1938, and synthesized in 1939. The exciting decade before World War II likewise brought the isolation of pantothenic acid (an important constituent of human enzyme systems) by Dr. Roger J. Williams (brother of the thiamine investigator) and the demonstration and isolation of biotin, still another essential enzyme belonging to the B vitamin complex. Finally, vitamin C, or ascorbic acid, the vitamin that prevents scurvy, was isolated in 1928; but it remained difficult to provide in medicinal form until a simple process for manufacturing it by fermentation was worked out in the mid-1930s.

At Upjohn, the process of making these vitamins available as nutritional supplements began with a combination of cod liver oil, malt extract, bone marrow, and iron called Myeladol, first marketed in 1930. Bone marrow and iron were traditional blood builders. The malt extract was included as the best source of B vitamins then known. Soon afterward, two other fluid vitamin combinations, Accessorone and Vitrate, with an extract of yeast instead of malt as the B vitamin source and cod liver oil concentrate as the source of vitamins A and D, were brought out. All of these were excellent sources of vitamins A and D, but they were at best a hopeful first attempt to furnish multivitamin supplements. The difficulty was that the concentration of B vitamins in crude malt and yeast extracts is low.

A major effort to overcome the difficulty was launched by Wise and the nutrition laboratory in 1934. Within a few years, several of the B vitamins would be available in pure crystalline form. In 1934, however, an improved natural extract still offered by far the best means of meeting the Upjohn objective—providing the physician with a potent B-complex source at the earliest possible moment.

In two years of intensive experimentation, Wise and the nutrition laboratory developed a yeast extract with seven times the B vitamin concentration of crude extracts. The new extract was put on the market in a combination with liver extract and iron named Cerelexin in 1937. Cerelexin tablets and syrup were the first products in the United States that made it feasible for the physician to prescribe large daily doses of B-complex vitamins. A liquid liver, iron, and malt-extract blood-building preparation named Jeculin for the treatment of anemia was also developed.

These products became important Upjohn specialties. But no one in the Kalamazoo firm could be satisfied with them. In spite of the deficiencies of existing A-B-D preparations, multivitamin combinations were popular with physicians and the public alike, both as a matter of convenience and because vitamin deficiencies in man were more often multiple than single. Products like Cerelexin were excellent and useful; but what was wanted was a preparation that could supply adequate daily allowances of all needed vitamins in a single daily dose, preferably in capsule form.

The nutrition laboratory accordingly began to prepare capsules containing vitamin A and D concentrates from high-potency cod liver oils, plus crystalline B and C vitamins as soon as these became available. Thus, in 1938, the Kalamazoo firm brought out Teleostol Compound C, a capsule combining A and D concentrates with crystalline thiamine chloride and ascorbic acid.

Teleostol Compound C was no great success in the drugstore. But the next year, the company developed a very small capsule—volume, about two minims, or just over a tenth of a cubic centimeter—containing the recommended adult daily allowance of vitamin A and D concentrate and crystalline thiamine, riboflavin, niacinamide, pyridoxine, and ascorbic acid. The product was blessed with a happily chosen name, Unicap, and was an instant success when sent on its way in 1940.

In keeping with Upjohn's position as an ethical drug manufacturer, Unicaps were not advertised to the general public. Nevertheless, they were soon established as the leading product in the vitamin field. Within a year, they were accounting for one-seventh of Upjohn's total sales; in 1942, they accounted for nearly one-fifth. Not in almost two decades had the Kalamazoo company developed a product that so precisely met a wide need, or was so quickly accepted.

Unicap vitamins are still the most widely sold ethical multivitamin product. Of course, the formula has been modified (and the capsule very slightly enlarged) by the addition of vitamin agents developed or discovered since 1939. Unicaps now include a daily allowance of calcium pantothenate (a form of pantothenic acid), and vitamin B_{12} (the anti-pernicious-anemia factor, isolated from liver in 1948 by a group of chemists at Merck and Company headed by Dr. Karl Folkers).

Numerous other vitamin products have likewise been developed. Only a few can be mentioned here: Zymadrops, a liquid multivitamin preparation, daily dose a few drops, for infants and small children; Zymacap, a high-dosage multivitamin capsule, for persons suffering from nutritional deficiencies or recovering from illness; Unicap M, a vitamin-mineral combination providing a recommended allowance of vitamins and minerals for adults; Unicap Therapeutic, a high-dosage vitamin-mineral combination; and Solu-B, a quick-dissolving freeze-dried sterile combination of B vitamins for injection in patients who cannot take nourishment by mouth.

The wide range of nutritional supplements developed by the Upjohn nutrition laboratory over the years has served two functions. One has been to help give the United States standards of nutrition second to none in the world.

The other was to stimulate greatly the Upjohn Company's

growth. Between 1930 and 1945, sales rose from $7 to $40 million a year. Fully half of the company's 1945 business came from nutritional products. Moreover, sales of nutritionals have continued to grow steadily, although they no longer represent so large a share of Upjohn's total business because of the development of other new products.

7 | A Problem of Succession

When Dr. W. E. Upjohn devised the friable pill, he turned to his family for help in manufacturing and selling it. He and his brothers held the chief positions in the company they formed. Relatives of varying degree filled other posts.

Many large American firms dating back to that period began similarly as family enterprises. Unlike most, however, the management of the Upjohn Company is still very much a family affair. Until 1958, most of the stock in the Kalamazoo firm—now become one of the largest pharmaceutical manufacturers in the world—was owned by the direct descendants of Dr. W. E. Although Upjohn has become a publicly held corporation, members of the family still own a large proportion of its stock and are conspicuous in its high command.

Family corporations often involve special problems. Not the least is arranging for the succession. In Upjohn's case, Dr. W. E. had long known whom he wanted as his successor. The head of the firm after Dr. W. E. was gone was to be his only son, William Harold Upjohn. But the problem of providing for the next generation in the Kalamazoo pharmaceutical firm's management had to be solved all over again in the last years of Dr. W. E.'s life, for Harold died suddenly in 1928 of an embolism following an operation for hernia.

William Harold Upjohn, born January 28, 1884, in Hastings, was a year and a half old when his family moved to Kalamazoo. As a youngster, his interests turned toward the graphic arts. By the age of ten, he had already developed a considerable ability as a caricaturist—an ability that was to be manifested in the caricatures he drew a dozen years later for the drug firm's first company publication, *The Overflow*.

Harold (as he was generally known) hoped to become an architect. His strong-willed father had other ideas. Dr. W. E. wished Harold to follow him in the Upjohn Company. It was 1907—when Harold was twenty-three—before he yielded to his father and went to work for the pharmaceutical concern.

Once in the Upjohn Company's employ, Harold worked hard for it. In college (which he did not finally complete until 1915), he took courses in bacteriology and other subjects to provide him with needed specialized background. In the company's offices, he busied himself not only with tasks of particular interest to him, but as an aide to his father.

One of Harold's special interests was statistical analysis. As already mentioned, he played a prominent part in the development of a distinctive method of market analysis. He was also active in the development of cost-accounting procedures, both for manufacturing and sales. Another interest was the design of company buildings. He and L. M. Crockett—who was brought into the Upjohn Company by Harold personally and who was an architect before he joined the pharmaceutical firm—were responsible for the White Office. Still another of Harold's strong interests was *The Overflow,* which he edited for several years.

As an assistant to Dr. W. E., Harold not only took part in the general management of the company but drew the pioneering plans for group life insurance and bonus programs for Upjohn employees. By 1925, he had convinced his tough-minded father that he was ready, both by experience and ability, for a more direct role in running the company. Harold was accordingly named vice-president and general manager, and Dr. W. E. went into semiretirement. Now past seventy, Dr. W. E. continued in the post of president. But his stays at his winter home in Pasadena and at Brook Lodge grew longer, and Harold was soon to have the presidency, too.

Harold Upjohn's life and Dr. W. E.'s hopes and plans were interrupted with terrifying suddenness one day in the fall of 1928. Harold underwent surgery for repair of a hernia. A few days after the operation, he developed a clot in a leg vein. A decade later, Upjohn researchers were to be instrumental in developing an anticlotting drug, heparin, for dealing with this complication of abdominal surgery, a complication that may lead to sudden death through "embolization," the breaking off and lodging of a fragment of the clot in the lungs. In 1928, no such drug as heparin was available. On October 15, Harold Upjohn died of a pulmonary embolism.

Dr. W. E. met the situation created by his son's death in a

characteristically direct way. There were several other men
in the company who might be considered for the presidency.
Before leaving for his annual winter visit to Pasadena, Dr.
W. E. instructed each to send him carbon copies of all his
office letters and correspondence. From Pasadena, 2,000 miles
from the scene of battle, Dr. W. E. watched how each carried
on the company's day-to-day business, as shown in his letters.
When Dr. W. E. returned to Kalamazoo in the spring, he
announced his decision. The man to be his successor as president was his nephew, Dr. Lawrence N. Upjohn, head of the
Upjohn branch in New York.

Dr. L. N. Upjohn was then in his fifty-seventh year. Dr.
W. E. therefore determined also to bring some younger blood
into the company. A younger man whose astuteness and all-
around business ability Dr. W. E. greatly admired was Donald
Sherwood Gilmore. Gilmore was both son-in-law and stepson to Dr. W. E.—a circumstance calling for a bit of ex-
planation. Gilmore was the nephew of John Gilmore, an
early Upjohn stockholder and, with his brother James (Gilmore's father), partner in a Kalamazoo dry goods store. After
the brothers died, James' widow Carrie ran the store and built
it into Kalamazoo's leading department store. The Upjohns
and Gilmores were neighbors, and widower W. E. (whose own
wife had died) married widow Carrie. A few years later,
Carrie's son Donald came home from Yale to marry a girl
who had been a childhood playmate and was now his step-
sister—Dr. W. E.'s daughter Genevieve. Gilmore then went
into the department store, and was its vice-president when
Dr. W. E. asked him to join Upjohn.

To Dr. W. E.'s surprise, both Dr. L. N. Upjohn and Gilmore were not easy to get. Dr. L. N. and his family had been

settled for twenty-five years in the East. He was not at all eager to pull up stakes and return to Kalamazoo, even for the presidency of the company. Dr. L. N. did not move back to Kalamazoo until some months after his election as president, on May 27, 1929. At the same time, Dr. W. E. became chairman.

It likewise took Dr. W. E. months to persuade Gilmore to give up retailing in favor of the pharmaceutical business. But on September 8, 1930, Gilmore—then thirty-five years old—began work at the Upjohn Company. His first task was reading incoming mail and discussing its contents with the heads of the departments to which the mail was addressed—a device hit upon by Dr. W. E. for swiftly introducing the new recruit to the Upjohn Company, and vice versa. In 1936, Gilmore became vice-president and general manager, and in 1944, president and general manager.

Unlike so many of his Upjohn relatives, Gilmore brought no special training in medicine or pharmaceutical production to the company. To this day, he professes to know little of technology or operating detail. Informal in manner and with the wise eyes of his Scotch-Irish ancestors, he says simply, "What I contribute is organization, systems of doing things." But that can take in a lot of territory. On the one hand, he is credited by colleagues with being one of the principal driving forces behind the expansion of research in the modern Upjohn Company. On the other, his was the idea for one of the pleasantest features of work at Upjohn today—the summertime thirty-five-hour week at forty-hour pay.

Another still younger man, who was destined to succeed Gilmore as president, also joined the Upjohn Company at this time. He was Dr. E. (for Everett) Gifford Upjohn, son of Dr. L. N. and another in the large number of Upjohns to be trained as physicians at the University of Michigan. After completing a residency in internal medicine, Dr. Gifford went to work for the family enterprise as assistant to the head of production.

Dr. W. E. continued to take an active part in the management of the Upjohn Company until a few months before the end of his life, when his health finally began to fail. Moreover, he even undertook a new project he hoped would prove "the most important thing I ever did."

Although the Upjohn Company more than held its own and escaped having to lay anyone off, Dr. W. E. was deeply concerned over the heavy unemployment brought by the Depression of 1929. He felt keenly the inhumanity of doing nothing for the unemployed. He had no liking for cash doles, for he held the conviction that the large-scale paying out of public funds without the production of goods or services in return cut the value of the dollar. A man with roots in the land, his preference was for a return to subsistence farming by the urban worker and his family during periods of slack employment.

Dr. W. E. determined to set up a model subsistence farming community for unemployed industrial workers from the Kalamazoo area. Beginning in 1930, he purchased some 1,500 acres of farm land near Richland, a few miles northeast of Kalamazoo. He pushed ahead with the project despite having to pay excessive prices for several plots of land he desired and despite the skepticism of members of his family, friends, and community and local union leaders. Repeatedly, it was pointed out to him that few industrial workers had the necessary farming skills and fewer still, a willingness to go back to the land.

Dr. W. E. never had an opportunity either to complete his plans or put into effect the central feature of the project. By 1932, the project was well along as a large operating farm. The latter was to serve, however, chiefly to provide part-time employment and supplemental cash income to unemployed workers living on subsistence plots on the farm. Each of the plots was to have a truck garden and a house, which the family living on the plot would help build.

The subsistence plot part of the scheme was never carried out. In fact, the only step Dr. W. E. was able to complete, beyond the organization of the central farm, was the establishment of a nonprofit foundation to administer the project and "to study and investigate the feasibility and methods of insuring against unemployment and devise ways and means of preventing and alleviating the distress and hardship caused by unemployment." He gave the foundation 10,000 shares of Upjohn stock (equivalent to 250,000 shares of the company's present stock, worth, in 1959, $12 million) as well as the farm.

The foundation operated the farm, known as the Upjohn-Richland Farms, as a commercial farm until 1958, when it was leased to the Upjohn Company for use as a veterinary research center. The gradual improvement in economic conditions in the mid-1930s largely did away with the need for the subsistence project. Instead, the foundation's funds were utilized to organize and support the W. E. Upjohn Institute for studies of unemployment and other economic research.

One weekend in October, 1932, Dr. W. E. spent several hours inspecting the farm project. A few hours later, he developed a throat infection. On the morning of Tuesday, October 18, he died at Brook Lodge of a heart attack precipitated by the infection. His age was seventy-nine, and he had been the moving force of the Upjohn Company for forty-seven years.

Nineteen-thirty and the years following brought the Upjohn Company not only a new president but numerous other changes as well. Although Upjohn's rate of growth was temporarily slowed, the Kalamazoo pharmaceutical firm was one of the few manufacturing companies in the United States able to report an increase in sales throughout the depression years. In 1929, sales were just under $7 million; the figure for 1932 was $8,500,000; the $10-million level was reached in 1935, and the $12-million mark, in 1937.

Several factors were responsible for the ability of the Upjohn Company to continue growing despite the depression. One was the fact that pharmaceuticals are a relatively depression-resistant business. Medicines are among the last items the consumer cuts back on in hard times. Another factor was the addition of important new products to the Upjohn line, particularly in the vitamin field; this was the beginning of the era of rapid advance in medicine and in pharmaceuticals. Still another factor in the company's continued growth was vigorous expansion of its sales effort.

In 1929, Malcolm Galbraith—who had been brought from the Kansas City branch to Kalamazoo at the personal suggestion of Harold Upjohn and who had been the company's unofficial sales manager—was given the official title of director of sales. One of his first acts was to press for an increase in the number of Upjohn branch sales and distributing offices.

Upjohn then had four sales offices, the same four that it had had before World War I: New York, Kansas City, San Francisco, and Kalamazoo. At Galbraith's urging, a Memphis branch was opened in 1931. In 1934, Kalamazoo sales and shipping were taken out of the company headquarters and made a separate entity, and in 1935–1938, branches were opened in rapid succession in Dallas, Atlanta, and Cleveland. The new branches produced a substantial increase in sales by greatly increasing the number of salesmen calling on physicians and druggists and by improving distribution.

The uninterrupted growth in sales made possible one of the Upjohn Company's most pleasing and remarkable accomplishments. In the seventy-five years it has been in business, the Kalamazoo firm has never laid off any employees (other than purely temporary workers, hired as such) because of cutbacks in production. It almost happened one winter in World War I—but it did not. At one point during the war, fuel supplies were so short that production had to be halted. The War Fuel Board allowed the company enough fuel, however, to prevent the plant and its equipment from freezing. Upjohn was accordingly able to keep male employees busy with repair and maintenance work; women employees were sent home, but they were kept on the payroll throughout the shutdown.

During the depression, the Upjohn Company was able not only to preserve intact its record of steady employment, but to maintain its program of insurance and vacation benefits and its policy of paying employees for a full forty hours per week, even when fewer hours were required to meet production schedules for a particular item. The principal effect of the depression on Upjohn employment policies was the imposition of a rule against hiring married women or keeping women on the payroll after marriage. The only exceptions to the rule were widows, women whose husbands were unable to work, and others in comparable situations. The rule—designed to spread work during hard times—was kept in force until the manpower shortage of World War II.

In Upjohn's early days, the hiring of employees was handled by Dr. W. E. personally or by the production manager or, in the case of salesmen, the branch manager involved. In 1913, however, a former minister, Franklin G. Varney, was added to the company staff to call upon employees who were in financial or other difficulties and to take charge of such activities as the company lunchroom (first started in 1910 with the serving of hot soup to employees who brought their lunches). Within a year, Varney was interviewing prospective male employees. By 1931, as employment manager, he had charge of the hiring of both men and women employees and a varied list of employee welfare activities. In 1937, a formal personnel department was organized, with Varney as the first director of personnel, a post he filled until his retirement in 1945.

Other changes took place, too. Among the most important were expansion of the research laboratories and the organization, in 1937, of a separate medical division, under Dr. E. Gifford Upjohn, to provide liaison between the company and the medical profession, furnish advice on labeling, sales literature, and the like, and, especially, to make arrangements for clinical tests of new Upjohn products.

In 1932, Dr. Heyl went to the directors of the company with a novel proposal for expanding Upjohn research. He suggested offering a series of fellowships to university re-

searchers in the medical sciences who were finding it difficult
to carry on their projects because of the depression. The
fellows would come to Kalamazoo to do the work. Projects to
be carried out might be in the area of either pure or applied
research; any results of commercial importance were, however, to be offered to Upjohn first.

A program calling for a dozen one-year fellowships on the
terms outlined by Dr. Heyl and paying the fellows $1,800 to
$5,000 a year each was announced by Upjohn in the spring of
1933. It had two effects. The first was to allow continuation
of significant depression-threatened research projects. The
other was to bring a number of the ablest young researchers
in the country to Kalamazoo. More than 570 applications for
the fellowships were received. The Upjohn research department was able to pick the dozen winners from a sizable proportion of the young investigators then engaged in medical
research in the United States.

The company was repaid many times over for the cost of
the program. Several of the fellows stayed on as regular employees after their year was up and not only contributed
numerous significant, commercially valuable discoveries to
the company. They were also instrumental in carrying Upjohn research into areas new to the Kalamazoo firm, such as
endocrinology. The fellowship program was so successful that
a series of fourteen similar awards was made in 1941.

The growing role of research in Upjohn affairs also received architectural recognition. When the research laboratories outgrew their original home—the 40-by-40-foot basement of the White Office—they were moved first to the "card
factory" (a one-time playing-card factory purchased by Upjohn in 1926), then to a building erected soon after the White

Office, Building 15. By 1934, it was apparent that the research division's twenty-eight employees and their equipment could no longer be squeezed into a corner of an existing building. So a 7-story Research Tower was included in the 13 stories of Upjohn's and Kalamazoo's tallest structure—Building 25, the massive building at the heart of Upjohn's downtown block, erected in 1936.

Meanwhile, the research division was carrying on work commensurate with its enhanced status. Particularly effective research was done in four areas of major importance, both to medicine and the Upjohn Company. One was the field of nutrition; the outcome of that has been described in the foregoing chapter. Another eventuated in the marketing of the anticoagulant drug heparin in 1942; the development of heparin is outlined in the chapter dealing with World War II. The other two involve sex hormones and hormones of the adrenal cortex gland. Pioneer sex hormone and adrenal cortex products were successfully marketed in the 1930s. However, prewar developments in both of these fields proved to be but a prologue to a host of remarkable advances in the years after the war. The sex hormone and adrenal cortex stories are accordingly reserved, along with accounts of other new Upjohn research, for later chapters.

8 | *Wartime Work*

Soon after the outbreak of war in Europe in 1939, many American pharmaceutical firms increased their shipments to Latin America and other overseas areas. The purpose—as during World War I, when much the same thing happened—was both to meet a need and to take advantage of the void created when the Allied blockade cut off the flow of drugs from the world-famed pharmaceutical and chemical houses of Germany.

Upjohn, however, made no attempt to increase its sales abroad during the war. Upjohn had an agency in London, and shortly after World War I, an effort had been made to introduce Phenolax into England under the name of Mylax. It was unsuccessful. Upjohn's export business thereafter was confined almost entirely to a very small volume of sales in Canada. Under Malcolm Galbraith as sales manager, the sales effort was concentrated upon the United States domestic market. When war broke out, the company decided against altering its policy. Aside from the lack of an effective export department, there was force to Galbraith's argument that Upjohn had realized only a small part of its potential United States sales. Moreover, as in World War I, Upjohn might have its hands full keeping established customers supplied.

Before long, Upjohn did have its hands full, but not quite in the way anticipated. The Kalamazoo company was hip-deep in orders and special projects for the Armed Forces. The United States was at war.

Most of the orders were for drugs and medicinal products, but not all. Along with other pharmaceutical firms, Upjohn received large orders for tableting a powder supplied by the Armed Forces. Neither Upjohn nor the other pharmaceutical firms was ever told what the powder was or what it was for; the finished tablets were simply identified as "chemical pellets." Word as to their purpose got around nevertheless. They were antiflash tablets, to be added to artillery powder to reduce flash that might help enemy observers locate Allied and American guns.

Shortly after Pearl Harbor, Leslie D. Harrop, Upjohn's general counsel, was told, on a trip to Washington, of serious trouble with the "hero" of Pearl Harbor—the sulfanilamide wound powder that had saved the lives of so many wounded and burned in the Japanese attack. The germ-killing drug had been believed to be self-sterilizing. It was not; it easily became contaminated with microbes against which it was ineffective. Furthermore, attempts to sterilize it had not been consistently successful; sulfanilamide is quickly caramelized by heat, the usual means of sterilization.

Harrop put in a telephone call to the Upjohn bacteriology department. Dr. John F. Norton, its head, thought the problem could be solved. In fact, he promised to—and did—deliver a kilogram of sterile sulfanilamide within twenty-four hours. Dr. Norton had accomplished the sterilization simply by very precise control of temperature and time during the sterilization process.

The result was a huge order, split with another pharmaceutical house, Hynson, Westcott & Dunning (which had devised the envelope), for sulfanilamide powder in special sterile envelopes—the famous wound packets carried by millions of American troops. Later, tablets of another sulfa drug, sulfadiazine, were added to the packet; to combat infection, the wounded soldier was instructed to dust his wound with the sulfanilamide powder and swallow the sulfadiazine tablets. Upjohn formulated and packed immense quantities of sulfonamides, in several different forms, right through the war. (Neither Upjohn nor Hynson, Westcott & Dunning, however, produced the basic sulfa drugs themselves; this was done by other chemical and pharmaceutical firms.)

Upjohn also filled large orders for injection ampoules of several standard medicinals, such as caffeine and benzoate of soda (a stimulant), emetine (the active ingredient of ipecac, a remedy for amoebic dysentery), and coramine (a respiratory stimulant). "We were asked for hundreds of times as many of some of these preparations as we had ever produced," recalls a man who was an Upjohn production executive at the time. "As a matter of fact, we were a little mystified because some of the drugs ordered were going out of favor with modern physicians. I guess they were ordered from prewar Army and Navy supply tables. There was a lot of that. The Armed Forces were expanded so fast after Pearl Harbor there wasn't time to bring all the supply tables up to date."

The Kalamazoo company likewise had an important, if unglamorous, role in two of the outstanding medical developments of the war. One was the introduction of penicillin, the other the development of medicinal products from blood.

Late in the fall of 1941, a series of fateful meetings was called in Washington by the Committee on Medical Research of the Office of Scientific Research and Development—the United States government's top wartime research agency—to consider a marvelous drug brought from England by Dr. Howard Florey of Oxford University. Discovered a dozen years before by Dr. Alexander Fleming of St. Mary's Hospital, London, penicillin gave promise of being the most remarkable antibacterial drug ever known. The catch was that the English could not produce it in quantity. Two years of backbreaking effort by Florey and Dr. Ernest Chain and their colleagues at Oxford had yielded barely enough penicillin to test the drug in a few score laboratory animals and five human patients—three of whom recovered from almost certainly fatal afflictions despite what would have been considered gross undertreatment by later standards. But, in grim 1941, England did not have the manpower and resources it would take to discover and put into effect a means of producing penicillin on a large scale.

British representatives asked for American help. A dozen experts said the evidence for penicillin's lifesaving value was too sketchy, the probability of massive difficulties too great to commit United States resources to an immediate all-out program to produce penicillin. The commitment was made anyway.

The initial program was directed toward finding higher-yielding strains of the microscopic mold that generates penicillin and toward cultivating the mold in deep tanks instead of the small flasks, in which alone, Florey and Chain had found, the balky mold would produce the precious drug. Most of the work was carried on in a half-dozen university laboratories and in pharmaceutical industry laboratories and pilot plants, and the industry furnished three-quarters of the nearly $30 million required to bring penicillin into mass production. The Federal government spent only some $7 million, chiefly for important basic research on the penicillin mold at the Peoria, Illinois, laboratory of the Department of Agriculture, for clinical tests of the drug, and for the construction of some penicillin production facilities.

Upjohn, which had had no experience in fermentation, was not one of the companies in the original penicillin program. By late 1942, though, enough penicillin had been scraped together to confirm English reports of the antibiotic's powers. The Committee on Medical Research determined that the United States must have at least some penicillin, even if efforts to mass-produce the antibiotic in deep tanks failed. Several companies were therefore approached to see whether they would build bottle plants to guarantee an emergency penicillin supply. Upjohn was one of five firms that agreed, although all knew that the plants might be obsolete before they were completed and would almost surely have little value within a year or two.

A small pilot unit was in production in the Research

Tower by June, 1943. By January, 1944, a full-scale bottle plant, set up entirely with Upjohn funds, was in operation in a rented building (later purchased by Upjohn) near the Kalamazoo railroad station. The bottle plant was in operation, delivering a modest but indispensable supply of penicillin, until 1946, when it was converted to the vastly more economical deep-vat type of plant.

The most trying of Upjohn's wartime activities was processing of the blood fraction serum albumin. Just before the war, Dr. Edwin J. Cohn and his associates in the physical chemistry department of the Harvard Medical School worked out a series of elegant procedures for separating blood into various fractions. The purpose had been simply to learn something about blood. The different fractions have different functions, however, and it soon occurred to Dr. Cohn that they might be used as substitutes for whole blood. For example, most of our defensive antibodies against infectious disease are concentrated in the gamma globulin fraction. Injections of gamma globulin can accordingly take the place of whole blood in bolstering immunity against ailments like measles. In fact, gamma globulin injections are much more effective because more concentrated. And, if the gamma globulin has been extracted in the right way, other parts of the same volume of blood are available for other purposes.

The serum albumin fraction of blood was of particular interest to the Armed Forces for use on the battlefield. When a wounded soldier bleeds, his immediate need is not for red cells but for restoration of the normal liquid volume of the blood. This can be accomplished with whole blood, but whole blood is too difficult to store and handle on the battlefield. Plasma (the liquid part of blood remaining after removal of the red and white cells) may also be utilized as a blood-volume expander and is much more practical, for it can be dried and shipped and stored without refrigeration and reconstituted with distilled water when needed. But plasma has drawbacks—it may harbor the virus of serum hepatitis— and distilled water is bulky. Serum albumin, a component of plasma, promised to be better. It does not harbor the serum hepatitis virus, and it is more effective in restoring and keeping fluid in the blood vessels; 1 liter of serum albumin solution has nearly the effect on blood volume of 2 liters of plasma. Thus, serum albumin reduces the amount of distilled water required for battlefield transfusions.

Upjohn had neither experience nor equipment for processing and handling blood and blood products. Both had to be built up from scratch. Nevertheless, the production department got the process for separating serum albumin from whole blood (collected by the Red Cross) "on stream" quickly enough. But batches of the Upjohn product inexplicably caused fever reactions in animals and volunteers in whom it was injected. A pyrogen (fever-producing agent) of some sort was getting into the serum albumin. Unless it could be eliminated, it would be impossible to use the Upjohn product.

"We really had a time on that one," recalls the man in charge of the sterile goods department at the time, Dr. Floyd A. Eberly, the Kansas-trained bacteriologist and chemist who became vice-president in charge of development and chemical production in 1958. "Try as we did, we couldn't spot where pyrogen was getting in." Dr. Cohn—a man not noted for patience or sweetness of temper and a power in the wartime blood program—threatened to have the Upjohn contract canceled.

Then the trouble was located. It lay in the transfusion sets packed with the serum albumin. Injection tubes for use with the sets were being allowed to dry after washing and before sterilization. This permitted bacteria to gain entrance to the tubes. Even though the bacteria were killed during the sterilization process, there was enough foreign matter in the tubes to cause the fever reaction. The reactions were eliminated by sterilizing the tubes immediately after washing. From this point on, the production of serum albumin went well, and large quantities were turned out.

Upjohn also produced gamma globulin and fibrin foam—a blood derivative useful for checking bleeding in surgery—during the war. Like serum albumin, these were wartime products only; they were discontinued soon after the end of hostilities. The wartime experience led, though, to one of the most unusual of Upjohn products, the absorbable sponge Gelfoam.

The research division became interested in the possibility of substitutes for blood products, prepared from raw materials easier to obtain and handle than blood. One line of investigation led to Plazmoid, a specially prepared gelatin solution designed to serve as an emergency alternate to plasma. Plazmoid was an effective blood-volume expander, but in peacetime, whole blood is preferred to plasma or plasma substitutes for transfusion. Plazmoid therefore never sold widely and was eventually put on the shelf.

Another line of research triggered by the wartime blood-product work had happier results. Surgeons have long sought something that could be placed in a wound to check bleeding and left there; ideally, it would be absorbed slowly as the wound healed, so that it finally disappeared after healing was far enough along to avoid any danger of bleeding. When fibrin foam was developed, it attracted immediate attention as such a material. But it proved too expensive and is another blood product apt to transmit serum hepatitis.

Upjohn researchers created an alternative from gelatin sponge, chemically treated to slow its absorption in the body. (Gelatin is ordinarily rapidly absorbed and broken down by tissue.) The gelatin sponge, called Gelfoam, filled the bill. There are many operations in which bleeding may be readily controlled with blood-vessel clamps and ligatures and in which Gelfoam is not needed—a fact attested by the gelatin sponge's modest sales volume. But in neurosurgery, in liver surgery, and in many other types of surgery, the absorbable gelatin sponge (which is nontoxic and causes no allergic reactions) made operation safer, simpler, faster. In the operating rooms where such surgery is done, Gelfoam has become literally indispensable.

During the nearly four years of active American participation in the war, the Upjohn Company produced about $15 million worth of medical supplies for the Armed Forces— which brought the company and its employees an Army-Navy E award on November 24, 1944—and several times that volume of products for civilian customers. The company's output climbed to an all-time high of $40 million in 1945— double the 1941 level. But profits did not rise in proportion. Government contracts were taken at little more than out-of-pocket cost and without full allocation of overhead expense.

The steep rise in output was achieved despite the wartime labor shortage and despite an unexpected change in production command. In 1943, Dr. H. S. Adams, director of production since 1930, died suddenly. C. V. Patterson, who had been appointed director of sales only a month before, was drafted to fill the vacancy. Patterson, a chemical engineer by training, performed brilliantly in the production post and went on to become executive vice-president and a key figure in the postwar Upjohn expansion.

While most of Upjohn's research men worked on war problems, some vital, independent research was continued. In fact, one of the most important of Upjohn research contributions only came to fruition during the war. This was the development of a practical process for producing the anticoagulant drug heparin.

In 1916, a Johns Hopkins medical student, Jay McLean, found that extracts of dog liver interfered with the clotting of blood. McLean's physiology professor, Dr. William Henry Howell, traced the anticoagulant effect to a substance he named "heparin" (from the root of the Greek word for liver). A dozen years later, Dr. Charles H. Best of the University of Toronto (co-discoverer of insulin) showed that heparin could be utilized to prevent the formation of clots.

Not long after Dr. E. Gifford Upjohn had become director of the Upjohn Company's newly established medical division, he suggested that heparin might have wide application in medicine if it could be produced in pure enough form to be safely injected into the blood stream. Dr. E. G. had in mind the prevention of postoperative blood clots, such as had caused Harold Upjohn's death. Another possibility was in the treatment of coronary thrombosis.

By that time, heparin had been found not only in dog liver, but in beef liver, beef lung, and numerous other tissues as well. Something had also been learned of its action. Heparin had no power to dissolve clots already formed; it prevented the formation of new clots by interfering with essential steps in the blood coagulation process. Only minute traces of heparin are ordinarily present in blood. Its function in the body appears to be the prevention of clotting in tissues bathed by fluids from blood.

In the mid-1930s, the only heparin preparations available —except for laboratory preparations of the anticoagulant— were crude extracts that were of interest to researchers but were too toxic to be used in patients. The problem of preparing a better extract was tackled by Dr. Marvin H. Kuizenga, a biochemist who had come to Upjohn on one of Dr. Heyl's industrial research fellowships to work on the extraction of hormones.

Dr. Kuizenga's starting point was a laboratory procedure for extracting heparin from fresh beef lung devised by university researchers. By modifying it, he was finally able to obtain sizable quantities of a highly purified heparin, suitable for medical use.

Heparin (now made from dried, defatted beef lung, a more convenient material than fresh lung) was released by Upjohn in 1942. It was the first of the large array of anticoagulant drugs now available to physicians (and chiefly developed after the war). It is still in wide use, although it has drawbacks in comparison with such drugs as Dipaxin (Upjohn's oral anticoagulant). Heparin cannot be given by mouth but must be injected every twenty-four hours or oftener, depending on the particular heparin preparation used. Heparin is, however, the only anticoagulant drug that takes effect immediately. When a patient has had a coronary attack and a second clot is feared, the doctor begins anticlotting treatment with heparin, though another drug may be used later; and when a patient has thrombophlebitis (inflammation of a vein, usually a leg vein) with active clot formation, treatment is generally begun with heparin. Moreover, heparin has come into wide use in connection with heart-lung machines and the artificial kidney and similar devices. It is one of the two drugs that can be used to prevent the clotting of the patient's blood in the machines. In skilled hands, the first anticoagulant drug is still saving a great many lives.

9 | The Long Hormone Road

Because science seeks to study the world in an objective, impersonal way, many dramatic moments in the history of science are glossed over and are soon lost to view. One such was the discovery of hormones.

It is hard to imagine a discovery in the field of biology and medicine more important than the revelation that the body has a system of chemical coordination and control based on a group of glands that secrete substances for regulating various bodily functions. The discovery of hormones has not only added greatly to understanding of the human machinery. It has disclosed the origin of numerous previously baffling ailments and provided the physician with powerful means for combating them.

Few discoveries have also had more profound effects on the pharmaceutical industry. Hormone products and derivatives are among the chief products of Upjohn and many other pharmaceutical firms. Research at Upjohn and in other pharmaceutical laboratories has been instrumental in developing hormone products and new hormone derivatives and in making them widely available.

Curiously, not many people, aside from scientists and physicians with an interest in the history of science, are fully aware of who discovered hormones or how the discovery was made. The discovery was a product of one of the most useful and charming friendships in the annals of science. The friends were two English physiologists of a half-century ago, Starling and Bayliss. While a medical student at Guy's Hospital in London, Ernest Henry Starling determined to make his career in physiological research instead of medicine. Not long after his graduation, he met a young Oxford graduate with similar intentions, William Bayliss.

Starling and Bayliss became lifelong friends and scientific partners. They complemented each other perfectly. Starling was lean, clean-shaven, and an impetuous man of action; Bayliss was rotund, bearded, placid, and reflective. Starling was a skilled surgeon; Bayliss had a flair for inventing apparatus. A remarkable team, broken up only by Bayliss's death in 1924, their joint efforts produced a steady flow of outstanding discoveries for more than thirty years.

The most momentous of the partnership's discoveries came on an afternoon in January, 1902, in Starling's laboratory at University College, London. A few months before, Starling and Bayliss had set out to investigate the workings of that little-appreciated but indispensable part of the anatomy, the small intestine. Most of the small intestine is concerned with the absorption of digested foodstuffs into the blood stream. The first parts of the intestine, however, the duodenum and jejunum, are involved in digestion.

Bayliss and Starling's first experiments confirmed a finding by Russia's great Pavlov that "peristalsis"—the wavelike motion of the intestine that propels food along the intestinal canal—is under the control of the autonomic (involuntary) nervous system. The two English investigators then turned to another question: What controls the flow of digestive juice into the small intestine? Whenever food arrives in the small intestine from the stomach (where digestion begins), pancreatic digestive juice also appears in the small intestine, and within seconds. How does this come about?

Starling and Bayliss guessed that the arrival of partly digested food from the stomach set off a nerve signal that triggered the release of digestive juice from the pancreas. To test this, they exposed the jejunum of an anesthetized dog and dissected out the nerves, leaving the jejunum connected to the rest of the dog's body by blood vessels only. Starling then injected a small amount of weak hydrochloric acid—a crude but effective laboratory substitute for partly digested food—into the denervated loop of jejunum.

To the surprise of both investigators, the injection was promptly followed by an outpouring of pancreatic juice into the dog's small intestine. The cutting of the nerves had not diminished in any way the response of the pancreas to the arrival of food or its equivalent in the jejunum. Starling repeated the procedure in a variety of ways. The result was always the same. Invariably, pancreatic juice was promptly discharged into the intestine.

Starling said at once that a "chemical messenger" must be involved. Starling's inspired deduction was quickly proved. In not too many weeks, he and Bayliss identified the messenger as a substance, which they called "secretin," generated in the lining of the small intestine. When food arrives in the intestine, secretin is liberated into the blood stream. The blood stream carries the intestinal agent to the pancreas and causes the latter to discharge pancreatic juice.

The discovery of secretin opened up the study of hormones. Men had long been aware that certain tissues are capable of exerting effects on distant parts of the body; castration has been practised since ancient times to fatten the steer, bend the ox to the yoke, furnish servants and guards for the monarch's harem. During the decade before the historic Starling-Bayliss experiment, moreover, doctors had become familiar with powerful substances generated by bits of tissue we now know as the thyroid and adrenal glands and had begun to explore their effects. But clear understanding came only on that afternoon in Starling's laboratory, with its revelation that the body has two distinct, though interrelated, systems of coordination and control— the familiar one based on the nervous system and a second one, chemical in nature. Starling's laboratory also provided the name by which the agents of chemical control are known. The word *hormone* was coined by one of Starling's colleagues from the Greek verb meaning "to excite."

Over the next five decades, scientific workers in many countries identified numerous additional hormones and endocrine, or ductless, glands (as tissues that secrete and discharge hormones directly into the blood stream have come to be known). It will make our story easier if we halt a moment and run quickly through the list, since Upjohn has been active in many fields of hormone research.

The testis and ovary proved to be the source not only of the germ cells that carry on the race but of secretions with specific effects on growth, maturation, and sexual function. During pregnancy, the placenta also functions as an active source of hormones, in addition to serving as the fetus's means of nutrition.

The adrenal glands—tiny tricorn-shaped packets of tissue sitting one atop each kidney—have been found to be double glands. Each has an inner and an outer part. The inner section, or medulla, produces epinephrine (one of the first hormones discovered) and a closely related agent, nor-epinephrine. The cortex, or outer section of the adrenal gland, generates an assortment of other vital hormones.

Still other ductless glands include the islet cells of the pancreas, which put out the indispensable hormone, insulin (other pancreatic tissues put out pancreatic digestive juice), and the parathyroids, a group of small glands adjacent to the thyroid that generate a hormone active in calcium metabolism. Recently, strong evidence has been found that bone marrow manufactures a hormone, erythropoietin, with an essential role in the formation of red blood cells.

And over all the glands sits the pituitary, the "conductor of the endocrine orchestra," in the famous phrase of brain surgeon Harvey Cushing. The pituitary is a small lobed gland situated in a recess in the skull just beneath the brain. The posterior lobe liberates hormones (probably generated in the brain, to which the pituitary is connected by a thin stalk) concerned in regulation of the volume of water in the blood, the contraction of the uterus during childbirth, and the release of milk during nursing. The pars intermedia of the gland, at least in some animals and perhaps in man, secretes a hormone having to do with skin pigmentation. The anterior lobe—the section of the pituitary Cushing had in mind in describing the gland as the "conductor of the endocrine orchestra"—produces hormones that govern other hormone-secreting glands: thyroid-stimulating hormone (TSH) to spur the thyroid, ACTH to stimulate the adrenal cortex, and follicle-stimulating hormone (FSH) and luteinizing hormone (LH) to stimulate the overy and testis. In addition, the anterior pituitary puts out a growth hormone with general effects on body growth.

Almost all of the hormones enumerated above, plus many hormone-like compounds that go far beyond nature in their powers and properties, can be purchased in the drugstore today with the aid of a doctor's prescription. For example, insulin extracted from the pancreatic tissues of cattle and other animals has prolonged the lives of tens of millions of diabetics. Thyroid preparations of various kinds have likewise been utilized by many millions of patients.

But no hormonal agents have come into such wide use or shown such an intriguing range of major medical applications as the group known as the "steroids." And in no area of medical or pharmaceutical research have Upjohn research scientists made a more significant contribution, either in terms of additions to knowledge or the development of practical medicinal products.

The steroid hormones are white, often waxy solids which take their name from possession of a common trademark—a chain of seventeen carbon atoms looped into four linked rings, termed the "sterol nucleus." For reasons that are still unclear, the sterol nucleus confers upon a great many of its possessors striking biological activity. Thus, cholesterol, one of the chief constituents of bile and a substance widely distributed in animal tissues (especially the brain and spinal cord), is a sterol nucleus with a side chain. Change cholesterol a little by opening one of the sterol rings and also removing a hydrogen atom from another ring, and the product is vitamin D_3. Attach certain complex sugars to the sterol nucleus, add an extra loop to the fourth ring, and you have the heart drug digitalis. Attach a fifth ring to the other four, make certain other relatively slight changes, and the result is methylcholanthrene, a compound with an extraordinary capacity for inducing cancer.

The steroid hormones represent still other variations upon the sterol ring theme. Two groups of steroid hormones have been recognized. One is composed of the sex hormones. As we shall see, sex hormones are produced in various forms by a number of tissues, but the chief ones are estradiol, the female hormone secreted by the ovary; progesterone, the so-called pregnancy hormone, a product of the *corpus luteum* (a yellow speck of tissue that develops on the surface of the ovary each time an ovum is shed); and testosterone, the male hormone, produced by the testis.

The other major steroid hormones are secreted by the adrenal cortex. A great many hormonal agents, including both male and female hormones and progesterone, have been identified in adrenal cortex extracts. The decisive products of the human adrenal cortex, however, are hydrocortisone, the hormone that counters inflammation, and aldosterone, a hormone essential to maintaining salt composition of the blood within vital limits.

Upjohn has had an active part from the beginning in the great scientific offensive that made the steroid hormones available to medicine, originally as crude extracts, then as pure chemical substances, and finally as chemically modified hormone derivatives with powers beyond those of the hormones themselves. The sex hormone story will be told first because, on the whole, it came to fruition first.

As in the case of high-potency vitamin D preparations, the Upjohn Company had to overcome an obstructive patent in order to enter the sex hormone field. By the end of World War I, research workers in several countries had become convinced that the ovary was the source of some sort of secretion with a role in the development of the female reproductive organs and in bringing female animals to heat. One of the investigators, Dr. Edgar Allen of Washington University of St. Louis, decided to undertake isolation of the putative hormone.

Dr. Allen had one requisite for the task. He had noticed simple tissue changes which occurred, generally within forty-eight hours, when ovarian extracts were injected into immature rats and which might be used to guide efforts to purify the hormone. But Dr. Allen was no chemist. For the chemical work involved, he accordingly enlisted the aid of a young instructor in biochemistry, Dr. Edward A. Doisy.

Their starting material was follicular fluid obtained from ovarian follicles containing mature ova. Dr. Allen believed that the fluid was particularly rich in the hormone. Several years of effort, however, yielded more potent extracts but no pure hormone. Follicular fluid actually contained less hormone than thought. And Dr. Doisy (who had meanwhile transferred to St. Louis University) ran into insuperable technical difficulties when he sought to carry out the final stages of purification.

A discovery in Europe came to the rescue. Urine from adult women was found to have female hormone activity, especially during pregnancy. So also was urine from pregnant animals. Urine, furthermore, does not contain proteins and many other hard-to-eliminate substances present in follicular fluid. Dr. Doisy quickly seized upon pregnancy urine as a much easier material to work with than follicular fluid.

In 1929, the St. Louis chemist was at last able to announce that he had obtained an active estrogenic hormone agent in pure crystalline form. Similar announcements came soon afterward from laboratories in Germany, the Netherlands, and Denver, Colorado.

The successful isolation of an estrogenic substance from urine and other current progress in hormone research created a stir in medical schools and among progressive physicians. Among those whose interest was aroused was Dr. E. Gifford Upjohn, who was completing his medical education while this was happening. After coming to work for the family company, Dr. E. G. kept up his interest in hormone studies— studies which were showing, among other things, that an estrogenic hormone might be very useful in treating menopausal disorders, menstrual difficulties, and other ailments of the feminine reproductive system. Even before becoming director of Upjohn's medical division, Dr. E. G. urged study of estrogenic hormones as a new field the Kalamazoo concern should look into.

By 1935, it had been learned that the estrogen extracted from urine was not actually the estrogenic hormone secreted by the ovary. In that year, Dr. Doisy and two colleagues succeeded in extracting a little more than a two-thousandth of an ounce of the latter from four tons of sow ovaries. The ovarian compound was a substance now known as "estradiol," whereas the urinary product is estrone. Estradiol differs from estrone in just one small respect: instead of an oxygen atom only, it has an oxygen and a hydrogen atom attached to one of the carbon atoms in the steroid nucleus—the carbon atom numbered 17 in the standard arrangement chemists have for diagraming steroids. The urinary product—estrone—is the form to which estradiol is converted probably after it has done its work in the body; in the language of biochemistry, estrone is a "metabolite" of estradiol.

Slight as it is, the difference between estradiol and estrone is sufficient to make estradiol several times as potent as estrone and one of the most potent hormones known. Recent calculations indicate that the average woman's ovaries secrete less than a teaspoon of estradiol in an entire lifetime. However, estrone is highly potent, too—it takes only a third of a milligram of estrone to match in effect the adult woman's daily output of estradiol—and estrone was what Dr. E. G. thought the Upjohn Company might produce. In the 1930s, estradiol was just too difficult to prepare for any pharmaceutical firm to contemplate manufacturing it.

Upjohn began by seeking a license to produce estrone under two estrone patents obtained by Dr. Doisy and turned over by him to St. Louis University. The university had already made licensing arrangements with a competing pharmaceutical firm, which had a prior claim for a license by virtue of grants that had aided Dr. Doisy in his work. The Upjohn bid was turned down as a result.

The Kalamazoo firm then did what several other manufacturers—likewise turned down on license bids—were doing. Legal and technical experts were assigned to study the estrone patents. Careful reading showed that the U.S. Patent Office had limited the patents to estrone of high purity, because many researchers had previously obtained potent though impure urinary estrone extracts.

Upjohn saw its opportunity. A group of biochemists under Dr. George F. Cartland, head of the pharmacology department in the research laboratory, devised a practical process for preparing an animal-test–standardized "estrogen crystallizate" from the urine of pregnant mares. To avoid infringing the estrone patents, the crystallizate contained not more than 90 per cent estrone, plus 10 per cent of other estrogenic substances also present in pregnant mare's urine.

The estrogen crystallizate was marketed under the trade name Urestrin. It was quickly successful. Many physicians preferred it to pure estrone because it contained other substances beside estrone; they felt—though there was then and still is no solid proof of this—that the mixture afforded a better guarantee of reliable action than the pure estrone extract. At any rate, demand soon outran the supply of urine that could be obtained from the Upjohn-Richland Farms— Dr. W.E.'s one-time unemployment project—where the Upjohn Company arranged to keep a herd of pregnant mares. The Kalamazoo company was compelled to buy crude extracts from outside laboratories; and it still buys them, for animals are no longer kept at the Richland Farms for hormone-production purposes.

Urestrin was but the first of a long line of Upjohn products in the sex hormone field. The next came right on Urestrin's heels. Interestingly, it was not another steroid, but a substance resembling follicle-stimulating hormone, gonadotropin, a hormonal agent secreted by the pituitary.

The story is full of surprise twists. Let us go back for a moment to the fact that the anterior lobe of the pituitary gland has much to do with the proper working of the ovaries and testes. This was first demonstrated by Dr. Herbert M. Evans and his associates at the University of California in 1922. Later, it was found that there are two distinct ovary- and testis-stimulating pituitary hormones. One, follicle-stimulating hormone, or FSH, stimulates the production of ova and the secretion of estradiol in women and the formation of sperm in men. The other pituitary secretion that affects the sex glands—luteinizing hormone or LH—spurs the production of *corpus luteum* hormone, or progesterone, in the female and of male hormone in the male.

FSH and LH have remained laboratory compounds. They have not been synthesized, and it has proved impossible to extract and purify them on a commercial scale. In 1928, however, two of the European researchers who had discovered the estrogenic activity of pregnancy urine—S. Aschheim and Bernhard Zondek of Berlin—found that human pregnancy urine also contains a hormone very similar to the ovary- and testis-stimulating pituitary hormones. The new hormonal agent was traced to the chorionic villi, the "roots" by which the placenta is attached to the wall of the womb during pregnancy and which also serve as the site of exchange of nutrients and waste products between mother and fetus. So it was called "chorionic gonadotropin."

The hormone actually appears in the urine in the first month of pregnancy, before the placenta is fully formed. It combines the action of the two pituitary sex-gland hormones and can be detected by injecting a sample of urine into an immature laboratory animal. If the patient is pregnant and chorionic gonadotropin is present in the urine, the animal promptly ovulates—a fact taken advantage of in the famous Aschheim-Zondek test for pregnancy.

It was inevitable that the chorionic hormone should attract the attention of pharmaceutical investigators. Though no one could be sure until supplies were available for trial, a hormone with the actions of the pituitary sex-gland hormones might have important medicinal applications.

At Upjohn, as soon as the basic work on Urestrin was completed, Dr. Cartland and his group went to work on chorionic gonadotropin. Since human pregnancy urine is not easily collected in quantity, the logical source was the pregnant mare. But the urine of the pregnant mare proved not to contain any of the desired hormone agent. By a quirk of nature, the kidney of the horse is unable to excrete chorionic gonadotropin. So it does not appear in the urine but remains in the pregnant mare's blood.

Dr. Cartland's group tackled the problem of extracting the hormone from mare's blood by an ingenious alcohol precipitation procedure similar to that which Dr. Cohn of Harvard was to employ and make widely known in the fractionation of blood during World War II. After collection, the mare's blood was centrifuged to remove the red and white cells. The plasma—the remaining liquid—was then treated with a reagent to adjust its acidity and alcohol added. At the right acidity, addition of the right amount of alcohol precipitates a nearly pure gonadotropic substance. Unlike so many other pharmaceutical processes, this one went well both in the laboratory and the manufacturing plant. The result was Gonadogen (the trade name for equine gonadotropin, Upjohn), one of the first gonadotropic preparations to become available for medical use.

Equine gonadotropin is not identical to human chorionic gonadotropin. In fact, it isn't really chorionic gonadotropin at all. It turned out to be pituitary follicle-stimulating hormone with some chorionic gonadotropin. But the mixture of equine gonadotropic agents has many of the same effects of human pituitary and chorionic gonadotropins, and can be used in their place. As anticipated, once Gonadogen became available, medical applications soon materialized. Most important is the treatment of disorders due to pituitary failure. One example is failure to ovulate or produce sperm; this may occur, as a result of pituitary deficiency, when there is nothing wrong with the ovaries or testes. Another is delayed puberty. Still another is cryptorchidism (undescended testes), in which treatment with gonadotropin can often take the place of surgery.

Over the past thirty years, the manufacture of hormone drugs has passed through three distinct phases. In the first —typified by Urestrin and Gonadogen—hormones were obtained from a natural source. In the second, they were prepared by what the chemist calls "partial synthesis" from readily available starting materials and, further, were produced in the form of esters or salts designed to introduce some desired property—for example, prolonged action. In the third —the present stage for several of the steroid hormones— chemists modify the hormone molecule itself, sometimes drastically, to create synthetic hormonal agents with further and more radical changes in properties.

A considerable overlap may exist among these stages. For

example, Upjohn today manufactures numerous synthetic hormonal agents. The research that led to them can be traced all the way back to 1941. At that time, the Kalamazoo company was still producing both sex and adrenal cortex hormones entirely by extraction, and the company had not yet got into the second phase (making hormones by partial synthesis or putting them into the form of new esters).

The latter did not come until five years after the war. During the war, Upjohn's hormone investigators were diverted first to a government-directed crash research program on adrenal cortex hormones (of which more in the next chapter) and then to the frantic effort to get penicillin into production. Work on sex hormones was not resumed until the penicillin program went over the top.

One of the first tasks, when hormone research began again, was to develop improved dosage forms. By 1945, male, female, and progestational hormones were all well-established drug products, but the forms in which they were produced left much to be desired. Available male and female hormone preparations were wasteful and fleeting in action. Most of the dose was excreted; to achieve the effects desired by the physician, doses had to be repeated at daily intervals or oftener. Progesterone was even balkier. It was inactive when taken by mouth and poorly absorbed and rapidly excreted when injected; large doses were needed to obtain any effect with it whatever.

The need for more easily used hormone preparations was made more pressing by the discovery of new medical applications for sex hormones. Of these, the most important was the use of male hormone in the treatment of inoperable breast cancer and of female hormone in the treatment of inoperable cases of cancer of the prostate gland, one of the commonest forms of cancer in men. Studies after the war showed that breast cancers are "hormone dependent," i.e., are stimulated by female hormone and can, in many cases, be held in check for months and sometimes a few years by treatment with male hormone; conversely, prostate cancers are often stimulated by male and checked by female hormones. Another major new hormone application was the treatment of fractures and "osteoporosis" (loss of mineral from the bones), a condition frequent in older people, with testosterone. Male hormone, recent research had shown, promotes the laying down of mineral in bones. Today, male hormone preparations are a frequent adjunct to the treatment of fractures, in older patients particularly.

A group of Upjohn investigators under Dr. Kuizenga and Dr. Arnold C. Ott, a steroid chemist, set out to find more useful hormone preparations by systematically preparing esters of testosterone and the ovarian female hormone, estradiol. "Esters" are a type of organic chemical compound corresponding very roughly to metallic salts like sodium chloride. For instance, sodium chloride may be formed by mixing the mineral base sodium hydroxide with hydrochloric acid; in somewhat the same way, many organic substances—including testosterone and estradiol—can be reacted with various organic acids, such as acetic acid (the acid of vinegar), to form esters.

Samples of many hundreds of esters of both estradiol and testosterone were made and investigated. The process was far more laborious than it sounds, for each had to be screened in animals—sometimes several species—for both toxicity and hormonal effects.

What was wanted was an ester that would provide a longer-acting dose and make less hormone go farther. An excellent one was finally found in the so-called 16-cyclopentylpropionate ester. Studies showed that active hormone was released but slowly from both ECP (estradiol cyclopentylpropionate) and TCP (testosterone cyclopentylpropionate) and that a single injection could provide effective hormone treatment for as long as four weeks. Introduced about 1950, ECP and TCP were the longest-acting sex hormone preparations yet devised, and they are still among the most effective to be had.

Around 1900, a number of biologists began to wonder about a speck of yellow tissue that appears on the surface of the female ovary in mammals, including man, each time an egg is shed. Ten years of experiments, chiefly in Germany and France, showed that the yellow speck, the corpus luteum, is a miniature gland that secretes a hormone essential to the start of pregnancy. The hormone, now called progesterone, prepares the uterus for pregnancy and aids the implantation of the fertilized ovum. But what further role progesterone might have was not clear. In 1936, however, Drs. Eleanor Venning and J. S. L. Browne of McGill University found that progesterone is converted in the human body to a compound called pregnanediol, which is easily detected in the urine.

As a result it soon became known that women produce large quantities of progesterone throughout pregnancy. The corpus luteum is the source only early in pregnancy; as the placenta develops, it gradually takes the place of the corpus luteum as the source of the hormone and keeps up the output until just before delivery.

The discovery raised a question that has haunted hormone

researchers for a generation. Though statistics in this area are hard to come by, as many as 1 pregnancy in 3 may end in a spontaneous abortion or miscarriage or in premature birth. Some miscarriages stem from malformation of the fetus. Some women, however, have repeated miscarriages, though their fetuses do not seem malformed, at least in any obvious way. Could miscarriage in such cases be due to failure of the placenta to secrete enough progesterone? Could the tragedy of repeated abortion be prevented by treatment with pregnancy hormone?

As of 1959, the question was still unanswered. In occasional cases, physicians have felt that an unborn child was saved by timely progesterone treatment. But the evidence has not been conclusive. The question could not be tested on a large enough scale, in part because of progesterone's cost and the difficulty of administering it in adequate doses.

In 1941, the Upjohn Company hired two steroid chemists, its first. During the 1920s and 1930s, Dr. Heyl and his associates had done considerable research on steroid substances, such as ergosterol, which are found in plants and fungi. Now it was time to undertake research specifically on the chemistry of steroid hormones. When the two new chemists—an Indian named P. N. Chakravorty, who was subsequently killed in a railroad accident, and Robert H. Levin, a graduate of the University of Wisconsin, a school strong in steroid chemistry —arrived in Kalamazoo, they were assigned as one of their first tasks research on a process for manufacturing progesterone by chemically reconstructing a more easily obtained steroid material, cholesterol. Progesterone had been isolated by four research groups seven years before by extraction from sow ovaries. Extraction was impractical as a method of producing the hormone commercially. The only logical way was by partial synthesis from some such material as cholesterol. Several pharmaceutical firms beside Upjohn, chiefly in Europe, were working on similar processes.

Upjohn's 1941 project furnished a small supply of progesterone concentrate for marketing a progesterone preparation and provided valuable experience, but it did not lead immediately to a feasible process for producing progesterone on a large scale. Moreover, when research on sex hormones was resumed at the end of the war, the disconcerting discovery was made that many improved methods of producing steroid hormones had been found, particularly by European firms just before the war, but were blocked by patents. It was more urgent than ever that the Upjohn Company develop effective steroid hormone manufacturing processes of its own. Some of these firms were known not to follow especially generous patent licensing policies.

In part because of the prewar progesterone project, in part because the pregnancy hormone was still a hard-to-come-by, potentially enormously useful agent, it was decided to concentrate the postwar effort upon progesterone. But this time a different approach was taken. A steroid material from soybeans, stigmasterol, was selected as the starting material.

Stigmasterol was chosen for two reasons. Soybean materials are readily available. There were, moreover, no patents in the way. In fact, it was commonly held wholly impossible to produce steroid hormones economically from soysterols.

The difficulty lay in a problem with which the steroid chemist lives day and night. The differences among steroid substances reside in atoms or small groups of atoms attached to carbon atoms in the various rings of the sterol nucleus, and especially in the side chain—a sometimes quite sizable group of atoms attached to carbon atom 17 in the fourth ring. To convert one steroid into another, it is necessary to alter the side chain and, usually, some few of the other attached atoms.

Living cells carry out such conversions, transforming one substance into another with ease with the aid of enzymes. For the human chemist, no task is more difficult. The problem is that his reagents are not selective or delicate enough. Instead of altering one or a few atoms, they are apt to destroy the whole molecule. In the case of stigmasterol, for instance, the conversion to progesterone requires, among other changes, cutting off one part of the stigmasterol side chain. The straightforward way to do this is to "burn" it off with an oxidizing chemical. But there are two other sites on the stigmasterol molecule that are equally susceptible to attack by oxidizing agents. If they are touched, the chemist winds up with a useless mess instead of progesterone in his test tube. Oxidizing the one site without touching the others seemed beyond the capacity of even sophisticated chemical procedures.

The problem was taken up by a group under Dr. Heyl, who had retired as Upjohn director of research but remained active in research for years afterward, and Milton E. Herr, who had come to Upjohn at the end of the war. After repeated failures, Dr. Heyl and Herr and their colleagues found an elegant way selectively to burn off the undesired part of the stigmasterol molecule. This made it possible to convert the soybean sterol quite directly into progesterone. The key steps in the successful development of the process were reported in three papers published in the *Journal of the American Chemical Society* in 1947, 1950, and 1952. Later, the economy of the process was greatly improved by two youthful Upjohn chemical engineers, J. Ward Greiner and Glenn E. Fevig, who found a way not only to increase substantially the amount of stigmasterol obtained from the ultimate raw material—crude mixtures of soybean sterols—but to obtain a by-product soybean chemical that Upjohn could sell to other manufacturers.

The new process was of great significance to Upjohn in two ways. To begin with, it came along just in time to provide a supply of progesterone for use in making hydrocortisone by a remarkable fermentation method developed at Upjohn and described in the next chapter. For another, it gave the company a dependable, economical means of manufacturing a hormone of outstanding importance in its own right, a means, furthermore, which could be applied to other materials, such as ergosterol, if the soybean material proved difficult to get.

Unfortunately, however, as far as the use of progesterone itself in medicine was concerned, having a good source of supply for the hormone was but half the battle. There was still the difficulty of getting progesterone into the patient in a convenient way and in effective doses.

Over a period of several years, many tens of thousands of dollars were invested by Upjohn in an effort to find an easily absorbed, orally active progesterone ester. The effort met with but limited success. One promising ester, 17-acetoxyprogesterone, marketed as Prodox, was found. It was more active by mouth than other progesterone preparations then on the market, but it was not so active orally as desired.

To obtain a progestational drug with the wanted properties, it appeared necessary to alter the progesterone molecule itself. Beginning about 1957, Upjohn steroid chemists accordingly prepared a series of progesterones modified in the various ways that had been found to multiply the power of cortisone and hydrocortisone. One of the modifications—worked out by a team under Dr. John C. Babcock—was the attachment of a carbon atom and three hydrogen atoms—a methyl group—to carbon 6 in the first ring of the progesterone steroid nucleus. A similar modification had been the key step in creating Medrol, Upjohn's high-potency, anti-inflammatory cortisone-type steroid.

The new progestational agent was 6-alpha-methyl-17-alpha-hydroxyprogesterone acetate or medhydroxyprogesterone, which Upjohn has trademarked Provera. It has proved to be the most potent progestational drug yet uncovered—hundreds of times more active orally than progesterone and, weight for weight, some fifty times more active by subcutaneous injection.

Provera was placed on the market in 1959. Time will serve to determine its full value in medicine. Ingenious new methods for testing the ability of hormonal agents to maintain pregnancy in the laboratory have shown that Provera (unlike Prodox, which exerted other hormonal effects but was deficient in this respect) possesses to a high degree the ability to prevent miscarriage and premature delivery in animals. Studies in pregnant women seem to confirm this in human beings, but further studies are needed to see whether it is really the long-sought means of dealing with a poignant human problem.

In any event, small doses of the new agent have proved effective in other, established medical applications of progesterone. Among them are the treatment of amenorrhea (menstrual failure), functional uterine bleeding, and other menstrual disorders (some of which may be treated with estrogen also, but some with progestational drugs alone).

While working on Provera, the Upjohn chemistry department went across the board and applied the potency-boosting modifications of the corticoid hormones to male and female hormones as well. One of the molecular alterations tested was the attachment of a fluorine atom to carbon 9 of the steroid rings. This "9-alpha-fluoro" modification had not been too useful in hydrocortisone; it multiplied hydrocortisone's anti-inflammatory potency but also increased the severity of undesirable side effects. But when applied to methyltestosterone, a derivative of the male hormone, it yielded an agent, 9-alpha-fluoro-11-beta-hydroxy-17-methyltestosterone, or Halotestin, with advantageous new properties.

Halotestin is a male hormone compound with five times the oral activity of methyltestosterone, hitherto the standard orally active male hormone. More important, two properties of great importance are especially enhanced in comparison with its masculinizing effects. One is the power to build tissue. Extensive clinical trials show it has about five times the power of methyltestosterone to build tissue in underweight, debilitated patients.

The other is the ability to retard and palliate breast cancer.

In trials at leading medical centers, Halotestin has been found to produce "striking objective improvement" lasting several months in a considerable proportion of patients with inoperable breast cancer. Other patients have experienced either some objective improvement, or relief of pain, or an increased feeling of well-being. Masculinizing effects, such as growth of hair and deepening of the voice, do occur in some patients but to a lesser degree than with earlier male hormone preparations. Only in a few cases have the side effects of Halotestin been so disturbing as to force suspension of treatment. At the time this book was written, Halotestin was, in the words of a distinguished physician and medical investigator, "the hormonal drug of choice in the treatment of advanced breast cancer and a foretaste of what the chemist can accomplish as he becomes ever more sophisticated and ingenious in manipulating the hormonal molecules provided by nature."

10 | To Cortisone and Beyond

In spite of the fact that the competitive system of business enterprise has been the subject of endless discussion and analysis (both hostile and friendly), one of its most useful and interesting features seems almost to have escaped notice. This is the ability to find a multiplicity of ways to skin a cat. As a result of competition among different business firms and different industries, one finds not only numerous competing electric refrigerators (for instance) and competing ads clamoring (sometimes all too loudly) for the buyer's attention, but also distinct and independent ways of producing a desired product. Thus, a great many products of the chemical industry—from dyes and detergents to paints and plastics—may be manufactured with equal ease from coal tar, petro-

128

leum, or vegetable raw materials. Thus, the community is not tied to any single source of supply.

As a consequence of competition and the operation of the patent system, many pharmaceutical products can also be made in a variety of ways from a variety of source materials. More than once, moreover, it has taken a multiplicity of means to meet the need for a valuable, hard-to-come-by medicinal product. A conspicuous case in point is cortisone and the potent group of hormone agents descended from it.

Although developments on the cortical hormone front now come with startling speed, they started slowly enough. A little more than a century ago, Thomas Addison, a London physician with rare powers of observation, connected the peculiar fatal disease now termed "Addison's disease" with atrophy or destruction of the "suprarenal capsules," the pads of tissue atop the kidneys we now call the adrenal glands. Addison did not know that the adrenals are double glands and that only the outer portions are involved in Addison's disease; in fact, he did not know that the adrenals were glands. This was not established until the discovery of epinephrine, a hormone of the medulla, four decades later; and the distinction between the medulla and the cortex— the inner and outer parts of the gland—was not clearly recognized until the discovery, around the turn of the century, that the two types of gland are separate in many species of fish. This made it possible to remove one part of the gland without removing the other and so ascertain that the adrenal cortex is the tissue indispensable to life, whereas the adrenal medulla can be dispensed with, perhaps because *its* hormones, epinephrine and nor-epinephrine are also secreted elsewhere in the body. (Why the adrenal cortex and adrenal medulla have come together in the long climb of vertebrate life up from the sea and are found as double glands in man and other mammals remains an unpenetrated mystery.)

The next step forward came when three teams of researchers finally succeeded, between 1929 and 1931, in preparing adrenal cortex extracts with unmistakable hormone activity. Drs. G. N. Stewart and J. M. Rogoff of Western Reserve University produced an extract that lengthened the survival of animals whose adrenal glands had been removed. Drs. Frank A. Hartman and Katherine A. Brownell of Ohio State and W. W. Swingle of Princeton and Joseph J. Pfiffner of the Parke, Davis pharmaceutical firm did better. Their extracts, prepared in different ways, proved capable of maintaining adrenalectomized animals indefinitely.

Although Addison's disease—the only medical application of adrenocortical extracts then in sight—is uncommon and the potential market for adrenal cortex extracts seemed small, Upjohn soon developed a strong interest in the field. Dr. E. Gifford Upjohn, especially, urged the company to begin research on adrenal cortex extract on the ground that any hormonal extract essential to life might well prove to have wider application in medicine. One of the first Upjohn industrial fellowships accordingly went to a young physiological chemist whose graduate work had involved study of adrenocortical extracts—Dr. Kuizenga, whom we met two chapters ago as he worked on Upjohn's process for preparing heparin. When he came to Kalamazoo in 1933, Dr. Kuizenga was asked to see what he could do about producing an improved extract.

In order to prepare a medically useful adrenal cortex extract, three problems had to be solved. One was elimination of the adrenal medulla hormone, epinephrine. An adrenal cortex extract was already on the market, but its usefulness was limited by contamination with epinephrine, a potent substance capable of causing severe reactions when injected into the blood or tissues. The second problem was to find an efficient solvent for extracting the active hormonal substances from the gland; the solvents previously employed in preparing cortical extracts were generally unsatisfactory as they also dissolved a good deal of inactive material, which then had to be removed. The third task was the hardy perennial of the medicine business—the preparation of a rigidly standardized extract, such that one lot would have the same potency as the next.

Dr. Kuizenga found satisfactory solutions for all three problems in surprisingly short order. Two were solved in a single step. He found that ethylene dichloride, the agent Upjohn was using to prepare vitamin D concentrate, was also an efficient solvent for cortical hormones and did not pick up epinephrine. Thus, troublesome epinephrine was automatically and practically completely excluded from the extract. In 1935, the Kalamazoo company introduced ACE, the first standardized epinephrine-free sterile adrenal cortex extract available for the treatment of patients.

In the Upjohn research laboratories, it was clearly realized that ACE was but a start on what promised to be a fascinating, but perhaps also a long road. Knowledge of the adrenal cortex was confined to the bare fact of its unique immediate essentiality to life. Loss or destruction of other endocrine glands may have grave consequences, but even loss of the pituitary or the insulin-secreting cells of the pancreas can be survived for some time. The adrenal cortex is the one gland whose complete loss cannot be survived (without cortical extract or hormone treatment) for more than a few weeks. But what precisely the life-essential functions of the adrenal cortex were, and just what substance or substances carried them out —all this was unknown.

During the next several years, Dr. Kuizenga, Dr. Cartland (the head of the pharmacology department), and other Upjohn research men worked on numerous aspects of the adrenal cortex problem. A strong interest was improvement of the animal tests utilized for assaying the potency of cortical extracts—an interest that led to the development of the Cartland-Kuizenga potency unit (which became the official potency unit for cortical extracts) and also brought to Upjohn for nearly a dozen years one of the best known of United States physiologists, Dr. Dwight Ingle, inventor of the rat-work test for measuring cortical hormones. Another major Upjohn interest was isolation of the hormone agents present in cortical extracts. Drs. Kuizenga and Cartland succeeded in isolating, in pure form, small amounts of several compounds with high hormone activity, including Compound E (cortisone). But they were a little late—in some cases, just a few weeks too late. Other researchers—notably Dr. E. C. Kendall and his colleagues at the Mayo Foundation and Dr. Tadeusz Reichstein in Switzerland—were ahead of the Upjohn team and got to key compounds first.

It is hard to tell just how adrenal cortex research would have developed, had the development continued in an ordinary way. But the question is now academic. In the fall of 1941, Washington heard a sensational rumor that made the adrenal cortex a matter of war as well as medicine and biology. The rumor was that German drug companies were buying adrenal glands from Argentine slaughterhouses to prepare an extract that allowed Luftwaffe pilots to fly and fight at 40,000 feet. The rumor ultimately proved false, but it gained substance from the fact—discovered about that time by a United States researcher—that cortical extracts increase the resistance of rats to altitude stress. As a result, the government set in motion a crash program of adrenal cortex research. The program involved twenty-one (Upjohn's among them) of the twenty-two laboratories in the United States and Canada that had done work on the adrenal cortex.

Much of what happened then has become widely known history. It was apparent from the beginning that it would be difficult, if not impossible, to obtain enough livestock glands to produce an "altitude booster" extract for the thousands of pilots in Allied air forces—if indeed cortical extracts had altitude-boosting effects. Further, it was doubtful that adequate test quantities of pure cortical substances could be isolated from extracts; the amounts isolated by researchers so far had been barely enough to identify cortical substances as steroids. Merck & Company, a chemical and pharmaceutical house strong in synthetic chemistry, accordingly undertook to prepare test quantities of cortical substances by chemical synthesis from more easily obtained starting materials.

For their first effort, Merck chemists chose Compound A (dehydrocorticosterone), one of the first and simplest substances isolated from adrenocortical extracts. Several hundred grams were prepared, at a cost of tens of thousands of dollars to Merck. (No government funds were involved in Merck's work on cortical steroids.) Compound A was a dud. It possessed no demonstrable useful biological activity in man.

By the time the results on Compound A were in, enough had been learned to make a cortical altitude booster quite unlikely and to cool enthusiasm for the entire project. Merck, consequently, decided to make only five grams of Compound E, on which its chemists had also started. Four of the five grams were sent, toward the end of the war, to medical investigators for testing in Addison's disease. Cortisone was quite effective in the adrenal deficiency disease—but another drug under test at the same time, Compound F, or hydrocortisone (which Upjohn had succeeded in extracting in test quantities from adrenal tissue), was better. Merck's last gram of cortisone went back on the shelf.

The last gram remained on the shelf until September, 1948, when it was sent to Dr. Philip S. Hench of the Mayo Clinic. A specialist in rheumatoid arthritis, Dr. Hench had been impressed for several years with the fact that women with rheumatoid arthritis often have remissions during pregnancy—a time when, other researchers had found, the adrenal cortex becomes hyperactive and puts out very large quantities of hormones. Dr. Hench had already tried cortical extracts without result; the best available were not potent enough. Now he wished to try cortisone.

Dr. Hench administered the gram by injection to two patients. There was enough of a response in both to send Dr. Hench to the telephone to ask for more cortisone and to send Merck's chemists back to their benches to begin reworking materials left over from the original cortical hormone project. Eventually, nearly a kilogram of additional cortisone was squeezed out—more than enough to treat the fourteen severely crippled patients on whom Dr. Hench and his collaborators reported at the famous rheumatological meeting in New York in April, 1949.

Cortisone is not usually found in human adrenal tissue and is not regarded as a true hormonal product of the human adrenal cortex. This distinction belongs to hydrocortisone. But the two compounds are closely related and have closely similar actions. The fourteen patients obtained relief from their pain and disease because cortisone and hydrocortisone have great power, along with other effects, to suppress inflammation.

The Hench report touched off an intensely competitive effort to find a means of mass-producing cortisone or some other substance with equivalent powers. The point was that the trial lots of cortisone had been produced from desoxycholic acid, a constituent of cattle bile, by a process so intricate most chemists were convinced it could never be carried out on a factory scale. And even if the bile-acid process could be scaled up, simple calculation showed that all the bile obtainable from slaughtered cattle would yield but a fraction of the cortisone required. For rheumatoid arthritis is not rare, like Addison's disease. It afflicts millions; and investigators soon found that cortisone's power to suppress inflammation could be utilized to advantage in a wide array of other ailments, ranging from eye inflammations to intractable asthma.

In due course, not one, but many prodigies of research and production were performed—enough to raise the pharmaceutical industry as a whole to a new level. Merck scaled up its "impossible" thirty-seven-step process and began to de-

liver modest quantities of cortisone early in 1950. Dr. Hench
and other physicians found that ACTH, the pituitary hormone that stimulates the adrenal cortex, could be employed
to achieve the therapeutic effects of cortisone; and chemists,
most notably those of Armour Laboratories, an affiliate of
the meat-packing firm, learned how to extract ACTH in
adequately pure form and considerable quantities from hog
and beef pituitaries.

Many other pharmaceutical firms were likewise busy with
adrenal cortex hormone projects. One of the busiest was the
company born of Dr. William E. Upjohn's friable pill.

As soon after the war as possible, Dr. Kuizenga and his colleagues resumed their studies of the adrenal cortex. One of
their first undertakings was a systematic study, with the aid
of improved testing procedures, of the hormonal activity
of extracts prepared from glands of various animal species.
The hog adrenal cortex was found to yield an extract more
potent than beef extracts in maintaining adrenalectomized
rats in a normal physiological state. It was found, furthermore, that a cubic centimeter of oil would dissolve and hold
twice as much active cortical substance as a cubic centimeter
of water. The product of these findings was Lipo-Adrenal
Extract, an oil solution of hormonal substances extracted
from the hog adrenal cortex. Introduced in 1947, Lipo-
Adrenal Extract had ten times the potency per cubic centimeter of the earlier Upjohn cortical extract, ACE.

The hog adrenal extract was presently to be overshadowed
by cortisone and other pure adrenocortical steroids. But it is
still in use in the treatment of adrenal insufficiency; and with
it, Upjohn investigators made significant discoveries. One

was the fact that the hog extract's high activity was due to a good concentration of hydrocortisone. This helped identify hydrocortisone, rather than cortisone, as one of the hormones of the adrenal cortex. Antirheumatic effects, comparable to those of cortisone, were actually obtained with Lipo-Adrenal Extract in a number of patients, though impractically large doses were necessary.

Another Upjohn finding was that potent adrenal cortex extracts were active by mouth, making it almost certain that cortisone and related drugs would be orally active, too. It was the Upjohn group that called this to the attention of medical researchers. Finally, it was Upjohn that supplied the first samples of pure hydrocortisone (prepared by isolation from hog adrenocortical extract) for clinical testing. And Upjohn chemists had a part, together with researchers from other institutions and a Canadian pharmaceutical firm, in preparing cortisone tagged with radioactive carbon for studies on how cortisone works.

But preparation of the radioactive cortisone and of the first clinical samples of hydrocortisone is a little ahead of the story. Dr. Hench's cortisone for arthritis bombshell put the Upjohn Company in a quandary. Upjohn had a position in adrenal cortex hormones, earned by more than a decade and a half of consistent research in the field. But it was clearer than ever that the day of medicines extracted from natural products was over. The future belonged to synthetic chemists who could begin, let us say, with cattle bile and wind up with cortisone. Unfortunately synthetic chemistry of that sophisticated kind was still comparatively new at Upjohn. A number of synthetic drugs had previously been prepared in the laboratory and manufactured by the Kalamazoo company.

But its first major development in large-scale synthetic chemical production—the manufacture of the B vitamin folic acid, by a process worked out by Dr. David I. Weisblat of the chemistry department—had just emerged from the pilot plant.

The burden of deciding what was to be done fell most heavily on two persons. One was Dr. W. E.'s stepson and son-in-law, Donald S. Gilmore, since 1944 president and managing director. The other was a bald, heavily built man, Dr. Richard S. Schreiber, whose arrival on the Upjohn scene in January, 1949, was no accident but was so timely as to seem almost providential.

In 1944, after thirty-one years both as active researcher and director of Upjohn research, Dr. Heyl had retired as vice-president and research director (though he continued to be active in the laboratory and indeed carried out one of his outstanding projects for Upjohn after his "retirement"—the synthesis of progesterone from stigmasterol). Dr. Heyl's successor in the top research post was a long-time associate, Dr. Merrill C. Hart, on whom fell the chief responsibility for the post-war expansion of Upjohn research. Dr. Hart, however, was only a few years younger than Dr. Heyl, and he had accepted the research directorship on an interim basis only.

A series of studies, both by company officials and outside consultants, led to a decision to go outside the company for a new research director. In particular, the pharmaceutical firm was after a man at once young and experienced in the direction of large-scale research—and with primary training in the new synthetic chemistry.

The search was led by Gilmore. Prominent chemists were consulted, and so were the heads of competing pharmaceutical companies. (In the pharmaceutical industry, Macy's will tell Gimbel's about a good research man.) The man whose name came up most frequently was Dr. Schreiber, a graduate of the world-famous chemistry department at the University of Illinois. Dr. Schreiber was then a research supervisor at Du Pont and clearly on his way up through the Du Pont research hierarchy. Gilmore determined to secure him for Upjohn, and land him he did. Dr. Schreiber first came to Kalamazoo as associate director of research and became director on Dr. Hart's retirement a few months later.

Dr. Schreiber hardly had time to unpack before his research generalship was put to the toughest of tests. The pharmaceutical industry was alive with word of the cortisone-for-arthritis discovery. The Upjohn Company had to decide what do, and at once.

Top members of the research division and Dr. Schreiber (who was still associate research director at the time) mapped out a massive seven-pronged program aimed at finding practical new methods of producing either cortisone or hydro-cortisone on an industrial scale. One group would work on a modification of the bile-acid method of producing cortisone employed by Merck. A second would make an effort to synthesize cortisone from simple raw materials, such as coal-tar chemicals. A third team would work on the chemical conversion of ergosterol, the easily obtained yeast steroid, to cortisone, and a fourth would seek to prepare the hormone agent from jervine, a steroid compound extracted from the root of the green hellebore, the common plant from which come the veratrum drugs recently used in treating high blood pressure. A fifth group of researchers would look into the possibility of preparing the hormone from accessible steroids with the aid of enzymes, as the hormone is prepared in the adrenal cortex gland. Another group would see whether microorganisms might be enlisted to aid in carrying out a particularly difficult step in the cortisone synthesis. And, as a final measure, Upjohn would take part in an expedition to Africa—one of six sent by pharmaceutical houses and government agencies—in search of the famous lost strophanthus vine, whose seed was reported to contain a substance from which cortisone might be made easily—if the vine could be found and cultivated.

The Kalamazoo firm decided to back the new research general and his program. Well over half of the 300 people in the research division were thrown into the cortisone fray. It was the biggest research gamble the company had ever undertaken.

Even the cortisone projects that failed make wonderful stories, and details will be given on some in a moment. But the stories will be easier to follow if we first acquire a bit of background on the chemistry involved in producing cortisone and cortisone-like compounds.

Although only small quantities of the many different cortical compounds had been available for study, it was known that the capacity of cortisone and hydrocortisone for suppressing inflammation depends on two particular attachments to the basic cortical steroid molecule. One is a hydrogen and oxygen group—a hydroxyl unit—attached to carbon 17, at the base of the side chain on the fourth ring of the steroid molecule. The other is either an oxygen atom or a hydroxyl group at carbon 11 on the third ring. Cortisone has an oxygen there, hydrocortisone a hydroxyl. Without these particular attachments, cortical steroids are of no value in the treatment of arthritis or other inflammatory disease.

The carbon-17 hydroxyl posed no great problem for the chemist; there were satisfactory methods of working it into the steroid molecule. The challenge lay in the carbon-11 attachment. Chemists knew of no reaction by which an oxygen or hydrogen-and-oxygen group could be directly linked to carbon 11 without disrupting the basic structure of the molecule. Merck chemists had dealt with the problem by making cortisone from a constituent of bile, desoxycholic acid, with an oxygen at a neighboring position, carbon 12; reactions for transferring it to carbon 11 were devised.

Like the efforts of other pharmaceutical firms interested in producing cortisone, the Upjohn program attacked the carbon-11 problem in two ways. Several of the projects had as their essential aim the discovery of a direct method of inserting an oxygen atom or hydroxyl group at carbon 11. Others sought natural steroid compounds with an oxygen at carbon 12, like desoxycholic acid or, vastly better yet, an oxygen already at carbon 11.

The search for the lost strophanthus vine was one of the latter projects. When research chemists begin work on a new problem their first stop is almost always the library, to see whether their purpose might be served by any of the hundreds of thousands of compounds other chemists have found in nature or made in the laboratory. When the cortisone seekers repaired to the library, they came upon reports of a plant substance with a crucial resemblance to hydrocortisone —and also upon a tantalizing mystery.

The name of the compound was sarmentogenin and it had a hydroxyl group right at carbon 11. It came from the strophanthus, a tropical rain forest vine from whose seeds central African Pygmies brew arrow poison. In 1915, Drs. Walter A. Jacobs and Michael Heidelberger of the Rockefeller Institute were investigating strophanthin, a digitalislike drug in strophanthus seeds, when sarmentogenin turned up in a single batch of seeds.

Drs. Jacobs and Heidelberger tested additional batches of seeds without finding any sarmentogenin, until, some ten years later, it turned up again in a batch of seeds of a different *Strophanthus* species sent them by a U.S. Department of Agriculture botanist. But then came confusion compounded. A second lot of the same species of seed contained no sarmentogenin.

European investigators had similar experiences. One team found sarmentogenin in two other *Strophanthus* species. Reichstein—the Swiss chemist who figured so prominently in the identification of the adrenal cortex hormones—isolated it from seeds of the variety originally studied at the Rockefeller Institute and also from the species given to the Rockefeller Institute by the Agriculture Department botanist. Then Reichstein and his associates systematically analyzed numerous additional samples of these two species of seeds. They could not find any sarmentogenin.

Since no possibility could be overlooked, an expedition was sent to Africa by Upjohn and S. B. Penick & Co., the world's largest supplier of botanicals, to see whether the *Strophanthus* with the 11-hydroxy steroid in its seeds could be located. The six-month expedition covered 11,000 miles through twelve central African territories and brought back cuttings, roots, and seeds of twenty species of *Strophanthus,* including one previously unknown. No sarmentogenin-containing seeds were obtained, either by the Upjohn-Penick expedition or any of the others.

Perhaps it was just as well. The exploring botanists also found the strophanthus vine an extremely poor candidate for practical exploitation. In its native state, the vine prefers the tallest trees of the tropical rain forest and bears its seeds 100 feet above the forest floor, nicely out of reach of anyone but expert Pygmy tree climbers. Moreover, it was extremely doubtful that the tall vine, a singularly fussy plant, could be adapted to domestic cultivation as a bush or in some other less awkward seed-producing form.

Although the search for the lost strophanthus proved an expensive waste of time, most of the Upjohn Company's other undertakings in pursuit of cortisone were not. For example, a practical method for manufacturing cortisone from bile was developed. It never advanced beyond the laboratory, but it was utilized to produce the sample of cortisone with which Mayo Clinic physicians found that cortisone was orally active in man. And trial lots of hydrocortisone were made from Compound S—an adrenal steroid that could be made from soy sterols—with the aid of ground-up adrenal cortex glands.

The approach that was to yield the richest fruit was the effort to put microbes to work in the manufacture of cortisone, as they were already at work in the production of antibiotics. The research division wound up with two teams seeking to harness microbes. One was in the endocrinology department, the other in the chemistry department. Both groups got started at almost the same moment.

The endocrinology department project was directed by

Drs. Kuizenga and W. J. Haines. One of its starting points was a suspicion that some of the hydrocortisone produced in ground-up adrenal cortex gland preparations might be the work of contaminating bacteria as well as of the gland tissue. At any rate, the Upjohn endocrinology group determined to put the question to test. Microbes that might act on adrenal steroids were sought everywhere that adrenal glands had been handled—in scrapings from slaughterhouse floors, in sweepings from Upjohn's adrenal cortex extraction plant, in dust collected in the endocrinology laboratories. Microbes were also obtained from microbiologists in antibiotics research.

In short order, two molds were found that could carry out that difficult step in making hydrocortisone—namely, attach a hydroxyl to carbon 11. The first microbe was a variety of Streptomyces, the family of molds that supplies man with so many antibiotics; it yielded small but measurable amounts of hydrocortisone when supplied with the steroid substance called Compound S. The second mold, a member of the genus *Cunninghamella,* was much better. It could convert Compound S to hydrocortisone with a yield of almost 50 per cent.

Curiously, this was not the process the Upjohn Company utilized as its main process for producing hydrocortisone. Another, even more remarkable microbiological process was employed. Work was nevertheless continued on the *Cunninghamella* process for many months, for Compound S could be bought commercially and the Kalamazoo firm wished to be sure of at least one workable manufacturing process for adrenocortical hormones.

The project that led to the process that was to play the major role in restoring Upjohn to its position as a leading supplier of cortical hormones was the work of a group in the company's chemistry department. Upjohn chemists already had considerable experience, gained in the effort to make progesterone, in methods of altering hormones by adding and subtracting oxygen atoms and the like—much the sort of problem involved in adding a hydroxyl to carbon 11 to obtain compounds from which hydrocortisone might be made. The chemistry department thought microbes might do the cortisone job, and more easily than chemists. The department, moreover, had on its staff a likely man to head the search for the proper microbe. He was Dr. Durey H. Peterson, a biochemist then in antibiotic research. As a graduate student in the 1930s, Dr. Peterson had worked with a widely known University of Chicago professor of physiological chemistry, the late Dr. Fred C. Koch, on the breakdown of urinary hormones by microbes. Thus, Dr. Peterson was already familiar with microbial actions on steroid hormones. He was asked to head a chemistry department search for microorganisms capable of 11-oxygenating or 11-hydroxylating steroids (as chemists term the process of attaching an oxygen or hydroxyl to steroid carbon 11).

Dr. Peterson was joined by Dr. Herbert C. Murray (microbiologist), Dr. Samuel H. Eppstein (biochemist), and other members of the chemistry department. To speed its work, the chemistry group utilized two new techniques, filter-paper chromatography and infrared spectroscopy, for assaying its brews for the presence of hormones. These gave results in hours instead of the days or weeks required for animal tests previously used. They also allowed more accurate estimates of the quantities of compounds produced, and they permitted the identification of compounds which were biologically inactive (i.e., could not be revealed by animal tests) but from which cortisone and hydrocortisone might be made. Thus, chromatography and infrared spectroscopy could yield more information than animal tests on what the microbes under study were doing.

The application of chromatography, particularly, to the search for steroid-transforming microbes took a bit of doing. Filter-paper chromatography is an elegant technique for solving a perennial problem of the research chemist—the separation of minute quantities of very similar substances. To carry it out, one end of a strip of filter paper is dipped into a solution containing the substances to be separated; the different substances will migrate up the filter paper at different speeds and so separate into distinct spots and zones. The substance in each spot or zone may then be recovered for separate study.

Filter-paper chromatography was developed in England shortly after World War II. In 1950, however, its application to steroids was one of the newest and most intricate wrinkles in chemistry. Very nearly the only men in the world who really knew how to chromatograph steroids were the two chemists—an Englishman and an American—who had worked out the technique of steroid chromatography. Upjohn sought to retain one of them as a consultant but found him already employed by a competitor. So Dr. Peterson and his colleagues had quickly to master the technique for themselves.

The effort to find 11-hydroxylating or 11-oxygenating microbes began with some moldy steroid samples found on a chemistry lab shelf. No molds capable of the desired reactions were discovered there. Dr. Murray then did what microbe hunters always seem to do, in real life as well as storybooks, because it is as good a way to search for microbes as any. He put open culture plates around the laboratory and on the window sills.

One of the window-sill plates caught a mold which proved quite efficient at hydroxylating steroids, especially progesterone, which Upjohn would soon have in quantity as a result of its new progesterone synthesis process. Some hours after adding progesterone to the mold broth, Dr. Peterson and his colleagues were able to recover nearly 50 per cent in the form of 11-hydroxyprogesterone. However, the mold also produced a form of progesterone containing two new hydroxyls per molecule, which was not wanted.

Although not too useful itself, the window-sill mold gave the Peterson-Murray-Eppstein team the lead it needed. The mold was a member of the Rhizopus family, a group of molds often found on rotten fruit and often suspected as a cause of allergy in man. The chemistry department group thereupon sent off to the American Type Culture Collection, a "bank" for microbes maintained in Washington, for other members of Rhizopus to test.

One of the species sent by the ATCC was ATCC 62276— *Rhizopus nigricans,* a most ordinary-looking white mold. *R. nigricans* performed almost beyond the researchers' hopes. Quickly and in high concentration, it converted nearly 100 per cent of the progesterone put into the broth to 11-hydroxyprogesterone, and it produced negligible quantities of other, less desirable compounds.

It seemed almost too good to be true. The microbial product did not have the 11-hydroxyl in quite the right position. It was in the 11-alpha (as chemists call it) form instead of the

11-beta form found in hydrocortisone. But the chemists were confident the 11-alpha-hydroxyprogesterone could be converted into hydrocortisone. In fact, Dr. John A. Hogg and his colleagues not only successfully produced hydrocortisone from 11-alpha-hydroxyprogesterone. They devised a process that made it possible to manufacture the high-potency newer cortical steroids, such as Medrol, from 11-alpha-hydroxyprogesterone as well.

There remained one unavoidable problem. Steroid compounds can be different, yet so much alike that they cannot be told apart by usual chemical tests. It was possible, though very unlikely, that the substance produced by *R. nigricans* was not really 11-alpha-hydroxyprogesterone, but a closely similar compound from which it would not actually be possible to manufacture cortical steroids.

The only way to be certain was by comparative tests of the *R. nigricans* product and an authentic sample of 11-alpha-hydroxyprogesterone with supersensitive instruments like the infrared spectroscope. But 11-alpha-hydroxyprogesterone was a new compound and the only way it could be compared was to convert it to a closely related substance, 11-keto-progesterone. A few researchers had made 11-keto-progesterone. One source was a research institute in New York. Unhappily, if Upjohn asked for a sample, word might leak out prematurely of the Kalamazoo firm's new route to hydrocortisone.

Upjohn decided it had to take that chance, rather than commit massive production facilities to a possibly useless chemical agent. The sample of 11-keto-progesterone was obtained. The 11-keto-progesterone obtained from the product of *R. nigricans* fermentation matched the sample in every particular. *R. nigricans* had indubitably produced 11-alpha-hydroxyprogesterone.

Ordinarily, pharmaceutical companies delay announcement of such discoveries as this until a product is ready for market in order to avoid alerting competitors. Upjohn employees were soon being asked, however, whether it was true a new route to cortisone had been found. The rumors even went across the sea. At a lecture in Stockholm, Dr. Dwight Ingle—then still with the company—was asked about the new process by a member of the audience. So Dr. Peterson and his colleagues were authorized to prepare a report for immediate publication. It appeared in the *Journal of the American Chemical Society* on April 7, 1952.

Upjohn came on the market seven weeks later with cortisone, and in 1953, with hydrocortisone, produced from the pregnancy hormone progesterone—itself manufactured in ever greater volume from a soybean material by the process originated by Dr. Heyl and Herr—by fermentation and chemical conversion of the fermentation product. In the meantime, investigators in other pharmaceutical companies had also devised other methods of introducing an 11-oxygen or 11-hydroxyl into the steroid molecules; and Merck and others had steadily improved the bile-acid process, making possible successive reductions in the price of cortical steroids. But the Upjohn process was sufficiently efficient and the necessary raw materials were easily enough obtained to allow the Kalamazoo company to inaugurate its sale of cortisone with a substantial reduction in price.

Either cortisone or hydrocortisone may be manufactured from 11-hydroxyprogesterone. Upjohn ultimately chose to produce hydrocortisone for several reasons. One was that it is highly effective when applied locally, or topically, as doctors say, in relieving inflammatory ailments of the skin or eye. Another was that hydrocortisone is a natural hormone of the human adrenal cortex and, weight for weight, is about 50 per cent more potent than cortisone in suppressing the symptoms of disorders like rheumatoid arthritis. Hence, smaller doses will do.

The greater potency of hydrocortisone not only represented an economy for the patient. Of greater importance, it offered hope of easing what was the greatest problem of corticosteroid therapy. When agents like cortisone are utilized in the treatment of, say, rheumatoid arthritis, they are usually prescribed in doses large in comparison with the quantities of hormone normally secreted by the patient's own adrenal cortex glands. In treating inflammatory disease, "normal" doses of corticosteroids have little useful effect.

Adrenocortical steroids, though, are powerful agents with a diversity of actions. Cortisone and hydrocortisone not only suppress inflammation. They slow down the excretion of salt and water by the kidney and promote the formation and storage in the liver of animal starch (glycogen), a reserve energy material; and the two hormonal agents may have other actions as well. These actions are also enhanced when cortisone or hydrocortisone is given to suppress arthritis and similar ailments. When long-term cortisone or hydrocortisone therapy is prescribed (as is often the case), unpleasant, even serious, side effects can result from other actions of the drugs.

It was hoped the greater anti-inflammatory power of hydrocortisone, as compared with cortisone, would be accompanied by a less than proportionate increase in other actions. Thus, patients might be more easily maintained on hydrocortisone than on the earlier cortical steroid. This was so, but the margin was not large. (It should be noted, however, that side effects have not been a problem when hydrocortisone is applied to the skin or eye, since little of the hormone is absorbed into the system through the skin or eye. Hydrocortisone ointments and ophthalmic solutions have produced excellent results and are still in wide use for many skin and eye ailments.)

As a result of the continued difficulty in treating ailments like rheumatoid arthritis, investigators began casting about for modifications of the cortisone or hydrocortisone molecule with altered properties. Interestingly, the first to be uncovered was found half accidentally. Chemists at E. R. Squibb & Son, an Upjohn competitor, found another microbial process for introducing an 11-hydroxyl group into steroids. When a suitable precursor material was used, the Squibb process yielded a compound very closely related to hydrocortisone, but completely devoid of biological activity. To convert it to hydrocortisone, the Squibb group utilized reagents that produced, along the way, forms of hydrocortisone containing a bromine or an iodine atom attached to carbon 9. Being good scientists, the Squibb investigators tested these novel compounds in animals. They were less potent than hydrocortisone, but active enough to lead the Squibb group to prepare hydrocortisones containing other members of the bromine-iodine family of elements at carbon 9. The fluorine member, 9-alpha-fluorohydrocortisone, was far more potent than hydrocortisone.

Unfortunately, fluorohydrocortisone was not useful as a systemic medicine; salt retention went right up with anti-inflammatory power. But the Squibb discovery focused attention upon cortisone and hydrocortisone variants formed in the several processes for producing the hormone agents. Two such were prednisone and its close relative, prednisolone. These differ from cortisone and hydrocortisone, respectively, in being minus a pair of hydrogen atoms (one each of the hydrogens attached to carbon 1 and 2) and in having a double link between those carbon atoms. The "predni" compounds were uncovered by researchers at Upjohn and at the Schering Corporation, who were among the first to put byproducts of the bile-acid process—of which prednisone is one—through chemical tests.

The predni compounds were a major advance. They proved to have three to five times the antirheumatic potency, milligram for milligram, of hydrocortisone, without a corresponding increase in salt and water retention. However, salt retention does occur in some patients treated with predni drugs. And the predni drugs had a new side effect. They caused sufficient excess stomach acidity to produce peptic ulcer in a number of patients.

At Upjohn—whose chemistry department was headed by Dr. Robert H. Levin, who had been one of the first steroid chemists hired by Upjohn—efforts to produce an anti-inflammatory steroid with fewer side effects than cortisone or hydrocortisone had actually begun before the discovery of 9-alpha-fluorohydrocortisone and the predni drugs. But now chemical research manpower was really put to the task.

The first step was the combination of the predni and 9-alpha-fluoro modifications in one drug derived from hydrocortisone. During the search for an 11-hydroxylation microbe, Dr. Peterson and his colleagues had turned up an organism (as had also been done by researchers in other laboratories) that converts hydrocortisone into prednisolone. Because the research division was completely occupied with other undertakings, little further study of prednisolone was carried out at the time. Now, the predni organism was used, together with chemical procedures, to turn hydrocortisone into 9-alpha-fluoroprednisolone.

The new compound was useless. Trial in animals—a tedious process requiring months—showed it to be, as steroid chemists say of a cortical agent that builds up salt in the body, "too salty."

Next, the Upjohn chemists went back to the original hydrocortisone molecule and tried tacking an extra methyl group—a carbon and three hydrogens—onto it. (The hydrocortisone molecule already had two methyl groups.) Adding a methyl to carbon 2 increased the saltiness of hydrocortisone. Adding it to carbon 6 yielded a compound with only moderate activity.

Now, a methyl was added to carbon 6 on prednisolone. The product was a compound, 6-methylprednisolone, with outstanding properties. Its anti-inflammatory activity was half again as great as that of prednisolone; at normal dosage levels, salt and fluid retention were nearly zero; and the tendency of prednisone and prednisolone to cause ulcers was greatly diminished.

The new cortical hormone was placed on the market under the name of Medrol. It proved not only effective, but free of a difficulty that has bedeviled other new adrenal steroids (including several developed subsequent to Medrol). It neither had the "old" side effects nor did it create new ones (like the ulcer-producing property of prednisone and prednisolone) to harass the patient and the doctor.

In common with other cortisone-like drugs, Medrol suffers from the limitation that cortical hormone therapy is suppressive rather than curative. For deep-seated, long-continued ailments, such as rheumatoid arthritis, specific preventive or curative treatment remains an urgent need. Prolonged, intensive treatment with any effective cortical agent, moreover, may produce "moon face," excessive hair growth, or other side effects in a proportion of patients. But within that limitation, several years of wide use have shown Medrol to be among the most useful cortical steroids to date.

The hour grows late, and the steroid story long. There is yet one more remarkable development to be related.

The preparation of compounds like Medrol means that the steroid chemist has succeeded in splitting off one of the principal actions of hydrocortisone—its salt-and-water-retaining effect. He would also like to split off hydrocortisone's "glycogenetic effect"—the boost that hydrocortisone gives to the storage of animal starch in the liver. That would bring the steroid chemist much nearer to his ultimate goal, an anti-inflammatory steroid with no other actions whatever.

Continuing their program of modifying the hydrocortisone molecule, the Upjohn steroid group in 1958 produced a compound with the predni, 6-methyl, and 9-alpha-fluoro modifications, plus one more—elimination of a hydroxyl attached to hydrocortisone's carbon 21. Fluorometholene or Oxylone—as the much-modified hydrocortisone has been named—has two highly unusual properties. One is that it is no more active than hydrocortisone when taken internally, but forty times as active when applied to the skin. So skin disorders can be treated with doses entirely too small to have any effect whatever even if absorbed through the skin. Thus,

Oxylone provides a uniquely safe anti-inflammatory skin medication.

The other extraordinary property turned up in animal tests. Doses of Oxylone that matched hydrocortisone in anti-inflammatory effect had only one-fifth of the natural hormone's effect on glycogen deposition. In other words, steroid chemistry has at last begun to split away hydrocortisone's glycogenetic action. Oxylone is not the drug that is anti-inflammatory and nothing else. But the research men who tailor molecules to order are clearly on its track.

11 | Architecture and Antibiotics

Dr. W. E. Upjohn once remarked that the Upjohn Company would require a new building every five years. His forecast proved far on the conservative side. In the $5\frac{1}{2}$ decades from the founding of the company to the outbreak of World War II, Upjohn had built or bought—chiefly the former—some thirty buildings for its home office and plant in Kalamazoo, or better than one every two years. All but the White Office and a few of the earliest structures were still in use.

By the middle of the war, it was evident that the Upjohn Company would soon need at least several additional buildings. It was not simply a matter of growth, although that was an important factor. As we have seen, the nature of pharmaceutical manufacturing was changing. Fermentation and
156

chemical manufacturing processes were coming in; new machinery and new procedures for mass-producing drugs in final dosage form were also radically altering the traditional functions of the pharmaceutical industry. Upjohn's downtown Kalamazoo site was not only lacking in space for expansion; many of the buildings were difficult to adapt to the new production requirements. A bold move was decided upon. Upjohn would build an entirely new plant.

During 1945, land was bought along Portage Road—an extension of Portage Street, one of the main streets bounding Upjohn's downtown area—six miles south of Kalamazoo. A total of 1,500 acres was purchased along both sides of Portage Road to allow room for growth, for parking and good appearance, for such necessary appurtenances of basic chemical manufacturing as settling ponds for the disposal of wastes, and for ultimate construction of an administration building across the road from the manufacturing area. Eventually, all manufacturing, sales, and general administrative activities were to be transferred to South Portage. The downtown area was to be turned over entirely to the research division and, in the modern pharmaceutical industry, research's close allies, the patent law department and the medical division.

By the time the administration building is completed, the whole vast project will have taken sixteen years and will have absorbed upward of $60 million. Long before completion, the project was to steer Upjohn in surprising directions. For instance, the pharmaceutical firm is now in the bus business. There was no way for employees without cars to reach the South Portage plant; so the pharmaceutical firm acquired a fleet of buses which ply routes to within four blocks of almost all employees' homes. At Portage, there is also a company-run seven-chair barbershop, which any employee is free to use on company time (haircuts only; no tipping, please). And Upjohn is undoubtedly the biggest operator of recreational facilities in Kalamazoo, with a movie theater, ping pong tables, shuffleboard alleys, and other games in the main plant building, and such diversions as a skeet-shooting and an archery range outside. South Portage is too far out of town for either noncompany barbershops or lunch-hour diversions for speedy sandwich eaters.

The Portage Road development consists of nineteen permanent buildings, including four manufacturing buildings, the administration building, and fourteen auxiliary structures. The first major unit to be finished was the antibiotics plant, rushed to completion and opened April 1, 1948, to take the place of the antiquated structure housing penicillin production downtown. Two months later, the adrenal cortex building, world's largest adrenal cortex extract plant, was put into operation. The next year saw completion of the power plant, designed to furnish 60,000 pounds of steam an hour for processing and heating (but no electricity). The fine-chemicals plant, the first part of which was opened in 1950 and which has been added to almost continuously since, came next.

The 33-acre main manufacturing plant, with its hundreds of thousands of square feet of receiving, storage, and shipping space, its huge production areas, its numerous glassed-in sterile-goods rooms, was formally opened on June 1, 1951 (though parts of the plant were in use before then). Finally came the administration building, ground for which was broken in 1958 and which was completed in 1961.

During the long period of its elaboration and construction, the Portage Road project—the largest construction project ever undertaken in the United States pharmaceutical industry —commanded the attention of many members of Upjohn's top command. Most intimately involved both in over-all planning and in the layout and installation of equipment was, of course, Upjohn's veteran vice-president for construction and engineering, L. M. Crockett, who has had a hand in the design and construction of nearly sixty buildings (including buildings for Upjohn branches) during his long career with Upjohn.

Another man with a key role in the project was D. S. Gilmore. In 1944, Dr. L. N. Upjohn, who had reached his seventieth birthday, switched from the presidency of the company to chairman of the board of directors. Gilmore, who had been vice-president and general manager, became president and general manager. Seven years later, almost at the moment of the formal dedication of the main manufacturing building at Portage Road, Dr. L. N. Upjohn retired as chairman of the Upjohn board and became honorary chairman, full of years and full of vivid recollections of the founding of the company and of the practice of medicine before the turn of the century. Gilmore then became board chairman and managing director; and the presidency returned to a man named Upjohn—Dr. L. N.'s son, Dr. E. Gifford Upjohn.

Gilmore was either president or board chairman of the company throughout the development of the Portage Road project. He enjoys building, and he looks upon the huge project as a major achievement of his association with Upjohn. At any rate, he took an active role in every phase of it, beginning with the purchase of the site, which, together with Crockett, he managed most opportunely for the company. And he had a leading part in selecting for the administration building a group of designers with reputations for highly distinctive work (Skidmore, Owings and Merrill, architects; Sasaki, the Japanese landscape architect; Virginia Conner Moseley of New York, interior design consultant). Thus he played an essential part in helping Upjohn to obtain a building that not only provides needed, efficient office space but is, through its unique integration of structure and terrain, a strikingly original and handsome building—and one of the all too few recently built United States office buildings not obsolete before the opening of its doors.

It has been remarked more than once in previous chapters that the history of many pharmaceutical companies and of the industry as a whole can be dissected into a succession of overlapping stages. The first was the compounding of botanical and traditional remedies. The latest is the tailor-making of potent new chemical substances for specific medical purposes.

The change can also be viewed in quite another way. Three decades ago, few pharmaceutical firms produced the basic substances incorporated in their products. They bought them, chiefly from chemical manufacturers and botanical houses specializing in bulk sales. For the most part, pharmaceutical houses were compounders. Today, there are many small firms that buy pharmaceuticals in bulk and package them. But nearly all large United States pharmaceutical companies both produce basic drugs and compound them into medicines.

The change came about largely because of the increasing scale and effectiveness of pharmaceutical research. A company's scientific staff would discover a useful new medicinal agent. Inevitably, the question arose whether the company should manufacture it itself; the question was usually answered in the affirmative. So the pharmaceutical firm became a chemical manufacturer. Several chemical firms have also become combined chemical-pharmaceutical firms in a somewhat similar way. Researchers in the chemical company laboratory would find a compound with useful medical properties, and the company would decide to compound it into a pharmaceutical as well as manufacture the basic material. Now the chemical company was in both the chemical and pharmaceutical businesses.

In many cases, such changes did not come without difficulty. For what was involved was nothing less than a decision, which had to be made by each company, to enter a new, unknown line of business. Such decisions are not easily arrived at.

In the case of Upjohn, the question was whether the Kalamazoo firm should undertake bulk production of basic medicinal materials on its own. The question arose at the end of the war and involved penicillin and streptomycin. During the 1930s, Upjohn had prepared its own estrogen and adrenal cortex extracts, but these were limited-volume products. Penicillin and streptomycin were required in much larger quantities. But the competition was rougher, too; Upjohn's competitors would include some of the largest and most efficient fine-chemical producers in the world.

As will be recalled, during the war Upjohn had set up a plant for producing penicillin by the bottle method to help guarantee an emergency supply of penicillin for the Armed Forces. Now, the vastly more economical deep-vat method was rapidly coming into use. The question was, What to do? Should Upjohn put in a modern type of plant or buy penicillin from other producers? Should the company market the

new antituberculosis antibiotic, streptomycin? Should streptomycin be produced or bought in bulk? (No patent problems
were involved. The basic penicillin patents had been assigned to the United States government, the basic streptomycin patents to Rutgers University, and licenses were freely
available.)

A considerable group within the Kalamazoo firm argued
for adherence to the traditional policy of purchase. The company decided, however, to stay in antibiotic manufacturing.
Deep-tank fermenters were installed in the place of the
bottles in the wartime plant, and an antibiotics building was
included in the plans for Portage Road.

But there were times when it looked as though those who
had wanted to stay out of antibiotic manufacturing might
have been right. Between 1946 and 1955, soaring production, plus the emergence (after 1948) of the broad-spectrum
antibiotics, such as chloramphenicol and chlortetracycline,
drove the price of penicillin down to 56 cents per 3-million-
unit vial, or less than 2 cents per dose of 100,000 units. (In
bulk form, penicillin was literally cheaper than the package
it came in.) A steep decline likewise occurred in streptomycin
prices; introduced at $20 a gram in 1948, in 1955 it was selling
for as little as 15 cents a gram. Many penicillin and streptomycin producers were forced out of the field. Production
of the two antibiotics ultimately became unprofitable to
Upjohn also.

The Kalamazoo concern chose to continue manufacturing
antibiotics after the war for two principal reasons. One was
that a purchase-only policy would have condemned Upjohn
to a permanent diet of scraps in the antibiotic field. It is the
patent story all over again. Upjohn would have been de-

pendent on the willingness of others to sell to Upjohn. If new antibiotics were found, they would be sold to Upjohn only after the companies that had discovered them had met their needs—and assured themselves of the lion's share of the market.

The second reason was the practical difficulty of operating an effective antibiotic research program, especially a program directed toward the development of new antibiotic products, without manufacturing facilities. New-antibiotic development demands extensive plant facilities. Moreover, it would hardly be sensible to discover a new antibiotic and then have to go to others for quantity production.

During the war, Upjohn had had a sizable group of chemists—some fifteen in all—studying the chemical structure of penicillin, the process by which the mold formed the antibiotic, and possible approaches to manufacturing it by chemical synthesis. Much research was devoted also to fermentation processes. Thus, by war's end, Upjohn already had a considerable antibiotic research program under way.

Unfortunately, it took nearly a decade for the program to generate a genuine head of steam. For one thing, little headway made on the synthetic penicillin project—either at Upjohn or in any other of the thirty-nine British and American laboratories that had been enlisted by their respective governments during the war in a vast effort to synthesize the antibiotic. The synthesis of penicillin by a practical, commercially applicable method was simply beyond the chemistry of the time. Very small amounts of synthetic penicillin were, to be sure, successfully prepared in 1946 by researchers at Cornell and Oxford Universities. But a method that could yield useful amounts of the antibiotic did not come along until 1954, when one was developed by chemists at the Massachusetts Institute of Technology.

It was 1955 before Upjohn's own antibiotic research program yielded a discovery of outstanding, immediate significance—the antibiotic Albamycin. Two products of interest were turned up, though, in the years after the war.

One was penicillin O, or allylmercaptomethyl penicillin, a penicillin variant for patients allergic to the usual form of the antibiotic, penicillin G. Penicillin O has enjoyed but limited use because it has, and confers upon the patient, a disagreeable odor and there are now many antibacterial drugs for patients who cannot tolerate penicillin. But, at the time of its introduction, there were few alternatives, besides penicillin O, for the penicillin-allergic patient.

Penicillin O, moreover, has an intriguing history. Just after the war, it was found that the penicillin mold required a compound named phenylacetic acid in order to produce the useful G form of penicillin and that the yield of penicillin G could be increased by adding phenylacetic acid to the fermentation tank. This led biochemists at Upjohn and Eli Lilly & Co. to try adding various other compounds to the fermentation tank. The penicillin mold obligingly incorporated many of them into the penicillin molecule, producing a variety of novel penicillins.

The new penicillins were not fully investigated at the time. A few years later, however, allergy to penicillin had emerged as a serious medical problem. Upjohn researchers—several of whom had themselves become allergic to the antibiotic while working with it—began seeking a nonallergenic form. Many variants of penicillin were tested, including several devised in the Upjohn laboratories. Penicillin O was one of the latter.

Penicillin O is produced by adding a special compound, allylmercaptoacetic acid, to the fermentation broth. Since then, that strategem—addition of appropriate precursors to the fermentation mix for the mold to hook into the penicillin molecule—has been used to produce additional penicillin variants, and the procedure has great importance for the future development of still other, ever more valuable forms of what is still the most widely used of antibiotics.

The other new antibiotic that came from the Upjohn laboratories before Albamycin was a novel one indeed. In 1946, Dr. Alma J. Whiffen and her colleagues in the microbiology department found evidence that an antibiotic active against fungi was present in culture filtrates from *Streptomyces griseus,* the mold that produces streptomycin. The antibiotic was soon isolated and a crystalline sample prepared for testing in a screening program operated by the Chemical-Biological Coordination Center of the National Research Council. The coordination center sent part of the sample to researchers at Michigan State University. The latter found that it was quite toxic to many plants but noted also that it halted an outbreak of powdery mildew among test bean plants. It was the first time an antibiotic had been found to control a fungus disease in plants.

This was the start of Acti-Dione (or cycloheximide, as it is also known), one of the most intriguing antibiotics ever discovered. Over the next several years, Acti-Dione proved to have remarkable powers against many plant diseases. Among those Acti-Dione controlled were cherry leaf spot, powdery mildew of roses and other ornamentals and also of several crop plants, a variety of lawn-grass diseases, and a number of fungus diseases of trees, especially the blister rust that has decimated many of the most valuable United States stands of white pine.

In the bacteriology laboratory, Acti-Dione has been found handy in isolating bacteria and in facilitating bacteria counts by suppressing contaminating yeasts and molds. And it has even helped a small number of patients with cryptococcosis, a rare, highly lethal disease caused by a yeastlike fungus touched by no other known medicinal agent. And in 1953, a research group at the Sloan-Kettering Institute for Cancer Research headed by Drs. H. Christine Reilly and C. Chester Stock discovered that Acti-Dione slightly but definitely retarded the growth of some varieties of cancer in experimental animals. The finding was a key factor in turning the attention of cancer investigators to antibiotics as a possible source of cancer chemotherapy agents.

But Acti-Dione did not establish itself as a major product until 1960. One difficulty was its toxicity. Acti-Dione is too toxic for use in human medicine except in desperate, no-alternative fungus disease like cryptococcosis. In addition, the unique antifungal antibiotic was expensive to produce. Originally, Acti-Dione was prepared as a by-product of streptomycin fermentation. Later, it did not even have the assistance of profitable streptomycin sales; as mentioned earlier, the bottom dropped out of streptomycin prices in the mid-1950s. Methods of application in one of its largest potential uses—the eradication of white pine blister rust—also involved formidable difficulties.

For several years, Acti-Dione enjoyed a slowly expanding

market (brought about in part by price reductions made possible by improvements in production) as an aid to home gardening. Then, two simple methods of application to white pine trees proved a success. One was spraying the lower 4 or 5 feet of trunk. The other was aerial spraying of an Acti-Dione derivative (Acti-Dione semicarbazone). A report from the U.S. Forest Service declared that blister rust could be eliminated from white pine with 3 cents' worth of spray per tree.

And more. Preliminary tests indicate that the novel antibiotic would prove effective in a long list of other fungus diseases of commercially valuable trees, including sugar pine, several species of southern pine, and Douglas fir. In the words of Homer J. Hartman of the U.S. Forest Service, the antibiotic uncovered by Dr. Whiffen and her colleagues represented a "major breakthrough" and had opened "a new era of disease control in forestry."

In the summer of 1955, the Upjohn Company sent a sample of a very promising new antibiotic, Albamycin, to Dr. Maxwell Finland, the well-known Harvard University–Boston City Hospital investigator of infectious diseases, for trial in human patients. Several months later, Dr. Finland called Kalamazoo to tell Upjohn that Albamycin had some striking similarities in performance to one of several antibiotic samples sent him by Merck. A short time later, Upjohn sent a sample of Albamycin and clinical data to the Food and Drug Administration in Washington together with an application for a new-drug license. Merck did the same with cathomycin (the generic name Merck gave the antibiotic Dr. Finland found so similar to Albamycin). Dr. Henry Welch of the

FDA put both the Upjohn and Merck samples through one of the chemist's favorite devices for identifying unknown substances, the infrared spectrophotometer. They were identical.

As happens so often in scientific research, two laboratories had independently made the same discovery. A few months later, Chas. Pfizer & Co., another large chemical and pharmaceutical manufacturer, announced the isolation of a new antibiotic, Cardelmycin, which also proved to be identical with Albamycin and cathomycin.

The discovery of Albamycin in the Upjohn laboratories was the fruit of a number of innovations, devised by Dr. George M. Savage, head of the microbiology department, that have greatly speeded the search for new antibiotics. In seeking new antibiotics, soil and other samples that might contain them are first incubated to increase the growth of any antibiotic-producing microbes present; then the sample is tested by putting it into cultures of various microbes and by determining which, if any, are inhibited by the sample. Dr. Savage's innovations simplified particularly tedious parts of the antibiotic-screening process. They permitted the Upjohn laboratories to isolate from soil samples and screen some 800 microbial cultures a week instead of 1,000 a year.

Albamycin was uncovered in a soil sample from Queens Village, in New York City's Borough of Queens, by a team led by Dr. Savage. It was produced by an organism identified as a new species of Streptomyces, the family of molds that has yielded almost all of the major antibiotics. (The Upjohn investigators named the new species *Streptomyces niveus,* and gave the antibiotic it produced the generic name of streptonivicin. Merck scientists, who also recognized their mold as a new species, called it *S. spheroides,* and gave the antibiotic the generic name cathomycin. Later, by agreement between the Upjohn and Merck research men, the antibiotic was given the generic name novobiocin, and Albamycin and Cathomycin were adopted by Upjohn and Merck respectively as trade names for novobiocin. The matter of the names of the mold or molds that were the source of novobiocin could not be settled until a novobiocin patent was issued. Then Upjohn's *S. niveus* could be compared with Merck's *S. spheroides* to see whether the two pharmaceutical firms had uncovered the same mold or two different molds that produced the same antibiotic.)

Tests showed that the new antibiotic had activity against at least as wide a range of disease microbes as erythromycin. More important, it was highly effective, both in the test tube and in animal tests, against that microbial villain of recent years, *Staphylococcus aureus*. A great variety of studies, both in outside laboratories and in Upjohn's own research division, showed that strains of *Staphylococcus* resistant to other antibiotics, as well as strains which were not resistant, were sensitive to Albamycin.

A new antibiotic must clear numerous hurdles before it may be marketed for medical use. Albamycin ran the obstacle course successfully. It proved safe in medically effective doses. It could be produced in large tanks by the deep-fermentation process that had been so useful with other antibiotics. And it was convenient to use; it was as effective orally as by injection.

Albamycin was introduced in June, 1956. Investigating physicians reported excellent results with it in ailments ranging from pneumonia to wound and skin infections caused by gram-positive bacteria—roughly speaking, the category of disease germs dealt with by penicillin. There was, beyond that, Albamycin's pronounced effectiveness against staphylo-cocci highly resistant to penicillin and other antibiotics.

Initially, Albamycin was reserved by many physicians to the treatment of resistant infections. In order to furnish an antibacterial compound of the widest possible activity and usefulness, Albamycin was combined with the broad-spectrum antibiotic tetracycline. (Upjohn had been purchasing tetra-cycline in bulk and marketing it under the trade name Panmycin.) The new combination, christened Panalba, ra-pidly became one of the most widely prescribed of antibiotic preparations. It was especially in demand during the winter of the great Asian influenza epidemic—1957–1958—because of a marked rise in cases of pneumonia caused by penicillin-and tetracycline-resistant staphylococci. Panalba was pre-scribed almost routinely in many areas in order to avoid re-sistant-staph pneumonia as a complication of the swift-moving influenza infection. To meet the demand for Albamy-cin and Albamycin-containing preparations, Upjohn at one point had to halt the production of all other antibiotics.

More recently, evidence has begun to accumulate that Albamycin may have a range of activity considerably wider than penicillin—in fact, nearly comparable to that of the broad-spectrum antibiotics. Thus, in a study covering almost 8,000 sensitivity tests upon disease microbes recovered from patients, Loyal S. Suter and Elizabeth W. Ulrich of the Veterans Administration Hospital in Memphis found more strains to be sensitive to Albamycin than to any other anti-biotic. Other studies have also recorded high Albamycin activity against gram-negative as well as gram-positive bac-teria. It may be that Upjohn's antibiotics research group un-covered an antibiotic even more useful than the group knew.

12 | Breakthrough on Diabetes

One day in 1955, a staff meeting of the Upjohn medical division heard a report from a member of the research laboratories on a project which he was carrying out in time allotted by Upjohn to all its researchers for work on studies of their own choosing. His undertaking was an investigation of herbs and other crude medicines reputed to lower blood sugar. He hoped to find a substance that might be of value in treating diabetes—perhaps a substitute for the hormone insulin, to which scores of thousands of diabetics owed their lives, but which remained an awkward drug to use, as it had to be injected and as proper dosage for individual patients could be difficult to determine. He reported finding several substances with enough insulin-like activity to warrant continuing his investigation.

171

The meeting took place on a Friday afternoon. The following Monday, a Detroit newspaper printed a squib reporting the discovery of a new antidiabetic drug, BZ-55, in Germany. Because of the discussion at the Friday meeting, the item was read with close attention in Kalamazoo. In addition, Dr. Earl L. Burbidge, director of the medical division, immediately telephoned officials of Farbwerke Hoechst—a West German chemical firm he had visited a few weeks before—to ask whether the report was true. It *was* true. As a matter of fact, Hoechst had an experimental antidiabetic drug of its own (BZ-55 was the product of a competitor) that seemed even more promising.

Dr. Burbidge was in Hoechst—the Frankfurt suburb where Farbwerke Hoechst is located and from which it takes its name—within forty-eight hours. Hoechst's drug—then known only as D860—was tolbutamide, now marketed in the United States and Canada as Orinase and elsewhere as Rastinon. Upjohn obtained an exclusive license to manufacture it in the United States. Finally proved safe and effective in one of the most extensive and carefully organized new-drug trials ever carried out, Orinase would usher in a new day in the treatment of diabetes and would become one of the most successful products in Upjohn history.

Chemically speaking, Orinase is a sulfonylurea, a compound related to the sulfa drugs, but not itself a sulfa compound. Its discovery caps as strange a tale of persistent failure to see one's nose in front of one's face as may be found anywhere.

For three-quarters of a century medical investigators—both legitimate and those touched with charlatanry—have been seeking remedies for diabetes mellitus (to give the high-blood-sugar kind of diabetes its full name; there is also a rare disease, diabetes insipidus, which has nothing to do with blood sugar and which we are not considering). Shortly before the turn of the century, there was a flurry of excitement over the discovery that large doses of aspirin lower blood sugar. Large doses of aspirin are, however, toxic. So aspirin proved impractical as a means of lowering the high blood-sugar levels the diabetic suffers as a result of partial or complete lack of insulin.

After the discovery of insulin by Banting and Best in 1921, the search turned to drugs that might be easier to manufacture and use than insulin. Literally hundreds, ranging from the commonplace to the bizarre, were tried. A considerable number showed some ability to lower blood sugar. But only two closely related compounds discovered in Germany in 1926—Synthalin A and B—showed enough to be at all widely used. Both proved dangerously toxic.

In 1942, an alert physician, Dr. M. Janbon at the eight-centuries old medical school in Montpellier, France, noted that an experimental sulfa drug, developed by a leading French pharmaceutical firm, caused an insulin-like reaction in several patients. A colleague, Dr. Auguste Loubatières, found that the drug indeed lowered blood sugar both in man and several species of animals. After the war, Dr. Loubatières, and other investigators also found other sulfonamides with insulin-like properties.

Many people were still interested in an insulin substitute. Yet, so far as known, no one undertook to screen sulfa drugs systematically for insulin-like activity. The next discovery was likewise an accident. Ten years after Janbon, a young West Berlin physician, Dr. J. Fuchs, administered another new sulfonamide, BZ-55, to patients with upper respiratory infections. Several of the patients complained of symptoms that sounded like insulin overdosage. So Dr. Fuchs—in accord with a strong tradition among German medical researchers —tried carbutamide (as BZ-55 is also known) on himself. Blood-sugar measurements clearly showed that BZ-55 had marked ability to lower blood sugar.

Now, finally, someone looked in the right direction. At the time, chemists at Farbwerke Hoechst were preparing novel sulfonamides and sulfonamide derivatives in the never-ending search for new antibacterial drugs. In a number of the sulfa derivatives, an amino group (one nitrogen plus two hydrogen atoms) found in all sulfas had been replaced with a methyl group (a carbon and three hydrogens). The change took these compounds out of the class of sulfa drugs and made them useless as antibacterial drugs. But one, D860, had a close resemblance to BZ-55. The chief significant difference was D860's possession of a methyl group in place of BZ-55's amino. D860 was found to have insulin-like activity and to be active by mouth. Moreover, since D860 was not a sulfonamide, it promised to avoid some side effects common to many sulfa drugs.

The availability of Orinase (as Upjohn promptly christened D860) through license gave Upjohn a good start toward an effective new antidiabetic drug. But there were many problems to be worked out. Would it really work in diabetics? Was it safe? To what extent could it be substituted for insulin? Which diabetics—if any—would benefit from Orinase and which not? Would diabetics become resistant to Orinase and have to go back to insulin? In short, the whole vast task of the clinical application of Orinase remained to be carried out—a task that was accomplished largely by American researchers and physicians, through the initiative and with the participation of the Upjohn Company and its staff.

The point is that there already existed methods of dealing with considerable effectiveness with diabetes, namely, diet and insulin. A good many patients with mild diabetes can be kept in good health for long periods of time by careful attention to diet (in particular, by minimizing carbohydrate-rich foods which lead to the formation of excessive quantities of blood sugar). More severe cases of diabetes can be controlled with insulin. However convenient, a new agent, such as Orinase, would have to be shown to yield results at least as good as those obtained with established methods of treatment. Evidence of safety would have to be especially solid in view of the bad record of previous oral drugs for diabetes. Otherwise, Orinase would not win acceptance; it would not get the Food and Drug Administration approval required, under the Food, Drug, and Cosmetic Act of 1938, for all new drugs.

The problem was compounded by the nature of diabetes itself. The insulin-deficiency disease occurs in two main forms: "juvenile" diabetes and "maturity-onset" diabetes. Juvenile diabetes usually sets in before the age of twenty and is marked by essentially complete lack of insulin. The maturity-onset form of the disease generally begins after thirty or forty years of age (most often in persons who are overweight) and involves a less marked deficency of insulin. Maturity-onset diabetes is more frequent than juvenile diabetes and is usually much milder; patients who can be treated by diet alone are found only among maturity-onset diabetics.

But maturity-onset diabetes can be severe, and both forms of the disease predispose—for reasons that are still a baffling mystery—to premature atherosclerosis of the blood vessels. Moreover, patients with either form of diabetes are subject to hard-to-predict alterations in status and insulin needs as their general health goes up or down. And with rare exceptions up to that time, both forms of diabetes were lifelong and required lifelong treatment.

The assessment of Orinase began with intensive animal-laboratory studies. The drug was investigated both in the Upjohn laboratories and by a small group of outstanding investigators in other institutions, such as Drs. Arthur R. Colwell, Sr., of Northwestern University; Jerome W. Conn of the University of Michigan; Rachmiel Levine of Michael Reese Hospital, Chicago; and I. Arthur Mirsky of the University of Pittsburgh. These studies not only confirmed German reports of Orinase's efficiency in lowering blood sugar, but they helped establish a key point. Orinase was found effective only in normal animals and in diabetic animals that still had at least some insulin-secreting cells. In animals all of whose pancreatic islet cells had been removed or destroyed and which therefore produced no insulin, Orinase had no effect whatever. This was a clear forecast that Orinase would be much more effective in maturity-onset than in juvenile diabetes.

Thorough tests of toxicity, both acute (short-term) and chronic (long-term) were also conducted. These showed Orinase to be singularly free of toxicity for laboratory animals.

All laboratory studies seemed to warrant a cautious trial in human patients. Beginning late in 1955, supplies of

Orinase were accordingly made available to a number of top United States diabetes specialists for tests in selected patients. Grants were also made for numerous special studies. Among those who took a prominent part in these crucial early clinical studies were Drs. Henry Dolger of Mt. Sinai Hospital, New York; Alexander Marble of the Joslin Clinic, Boston; and Sol Sherry of Washington University of St. Louis.

As experience in the treatment of diabetes with Orinase was gained, the scope of the trial—which was under the over-all direction of Dr. C. J. O'Donovan of the medical division—was extended. More special studies were carried out, and supplies of Orinase were made available to larger groups of diabetes specialists, and then even to general practitioners with experience in treating diabetes. Nineteen tons of Orinase—enough for nearly a million and a half doses—had been given away by the time Upjohn received clearance to place it on sale in June, 1957. Some 20,000 diabetics in all parts of the country and with virtually all possible variations of the disease had received Orinase for periods of several weeks to a year and a half or more. Detailed reports on 9,168 patients had been sent by 420 physicians to Kalamazoo, where they were collated and analyzed by specially installed electronic data-processing equipment.

What did this massive assessment show? First, the lack of toxicity found in animal studies applies also to man. Both in clinical trial and since, Orinase has proved itself one of the safest drugs ever developed. A good many of the drugs on which we depend for fighting disease can do subtle damage, especially if misused, to the blood-forming tissues of the bone marrow. Bone marrow damage has not occurred with Orinase. Nor has any evidence of injury to other vital organs been encountered. Other side effects have been mild and infrequent. Side effects of any kind occur in no more than 1.5 per cent of patients—about the percentage of patients who report side effects while taking placebo (dummy) pills—and have been confined to skin rashes, itching, and mild gastrointestinal disturbances, which soon disappear in many cases even when Orinase treatment is continued.

The clinical trial also bore out the laboratory studies on the type of diabetes in which Orinase would be most effective. The oral antidiabetic was found to work best in patients with maturity-onset diabetes who need no or moderate amounts of insulin and who have no history of diabetic complications. Physicians reported restoration of blood sugar essentially to normal and control of other diabetic symptoms by Orinase in 70 to as high as 95 per cent of such patients. Patients who still needed insulin after being put on Orinase also benefited, though to a lesser extent; about 50 per cent achieved better control with less insulin. Juvenile diabetics, on the other hand, were only occasionally helped by Orinase. In sum—since maturity-onset diabetes represents about three-quarters of cases of diabetes—the new drug can be employed with good effect in half or more of all diabetics.

In many patients, Orinase has brought better control than could be achieved by either diet or insulin. Dr. Dolger tells of a seventy-nine-year-old man whose diabetes began in 1904. Before insulin, he was treated by diet; after insulin, by diet plus 30 units of insulin a day. He was switched to Orinase, at his insistence, in 1956. Within a few days, his blood sugar was completely normal and his urine wholly free of sugar—a record never accomplished with insulin.

Soon after the start of the Orinase trial, patients who successfully made the switch from insulin began reporting that they felt much better on the new drug. Aside from enjoyment of their new freedom from the needle, they noticed an end to the spells of faintness so common among patients taking insulin. These spells occur because insulin injections generally take effect quickly and can drive the blood sugar down too far—all the way to zero, in fact. Such "hypoglycemic reactions" are the reason why diabetics are disqualified for many jobs and why they keep fruit juice or some other quick source of sugar handy when they take insulin. Orinase, on the other hand, takes about five hours to produce its peak effect on blood sugar in diabetics—long enough for mealtime to come around first and provide the diabetic with something to offset any possible hypoglycemia.

It turns out, moreover, that Orinase contains a built-in safety brake against severe hypoglycemic reactions. When the dosage of Orinase is increased from the usual 1 or 1.5 to 3 grams a day, there is a moderate increase in the effect on the blood sugar. Further increases in dose—even large ones, while further lowering blood sugar, rarely cause severe hypoglycemic reactions.

During and since the clinical trial, numerous physicians have attempted to work out criteria or sets of rules for selecting patients for Orinase treatment. Some thought it ought to be restricted to patients with diabetes of recent origin. Others believed the new antidiabetic agent should not be used in combination with insulin, i.e., should not be given to patients who might still need some insulin. Still others suggested other criteria. Time has shown that it would be unwise to apply most of these rules strictly, for they would exclude from Orinase therapy many who would benefit from it greatly. Increasingly, physicians are simply giving Orinase a trial in all patients with maturity-onset diabetes and no record of such complications as diabetic acidosis. In a substantial majority of cases, the oral antidiabetic is achieving highly satisfactory results, with less discomfort than the insulin-taking patient has ever known.

When Orinase was first announced, it was widely stated that its real significance lay not in what it might do for patients, but in the stimulus it would give to research on diabetes. Patients who have been helped by tolbutamide might disagree. Nevertheless, the oral antidiabetic has been a powerful spur to research on diabetes, research which is yielding striking new information on the nature of the disease. For instance, recent studies with Orinase indicate that diabetes mellitus—whose underlying cause is still a mystery—may well be not one disease, but two.

Almost from the moment of its discovery, investigators in many parts of the world have sought to learn how Orinase works. As has been mentioned, it was quickly found that Orinase lowers blood sugar only in animals and human patients who can produce at least some insulin. In animals whose pancreatic islet tissue has been entirely removed or destroyed and in human patients with complete failure of the insulin-forming tissues, Orinase is wholly inactive.

This led to two main theories of Orinase action. One was that the new antidiabetic agent promoted the release of insulin from the pancreatic cells where it is formed. The other was that Orinase offset an insulin-blocking agent—an "insulinase"—which might be present in diabetics and which might prevent insulin from carrying out its normal functions.

Today, it is probable that the main action of tolbutamide is to facilitate the release of insulin from the pancreas. The researches by which this conclusion was reached are too intricate to be spelled out here. However, several investigators (especially Dr. Solomon A. Berson of the Kingsbridge Veterans Hospital, New York, who did so in a particularly elegant way) have succeeded in measuring changes in the amount of insulin in the blood induced by Orinase, both in normal individuals and diabetics. Experts say these studies can only mean that Orinase speeds the release of insulin from the pancreas.

More dramatic is the evidence offered by the research of Drs. Paul E. Lacy and W. Stanley Hartroft of Washington University of St. Louis. Insulin is found in pancreatic islet cells in two forms, one soluble, and the other in the form of granules, in which it is held in storage, to be released as needed. The Washington University investigators made electron microscope photographs of islet cells under a variety of conditions. Some of the photographs show the strikingly different forms the insulin granules assume in different species (those of a rat are round; of a dog, rectangular; and of a chicken, needle-shaped). Several show the disappearance of the insulin granules after a large dose of sugar. And several clearly reveal the emptying of the granule sacs after a dose of Orinase.

The important point of these findings is that they make it highly probable that juvenile diabetes and maturity-onset diabetes are not simply, as has often been thought, different forms of the same disease, but different diseases, with a different origin and requiring different methods of treatment. In juvenile diabetes—the kind in which Orinase is only occasionally helpful—the primary difficulty is inability to form insulin. In maturity-onset diabetes—at least in those cases that respond to Orinase—the chief difficulty is insulin release. In these patients, the pancreatic islet cells generate sizable quantities of insulin, but for some reason, the insulin is not discharged into the bloodstream as needed. So these persons become diabetic.

Early in the clinical trial of Orinase, a number of investigators asked Upjohn to prepare Orinase in injectable form for a variety of special studies. The task was not difficult. Samples of the antidiabetic in a form suitable for injection were soon ready. The injectable Orinase was wanted for the development of a rapid test for singling out diabetics who could be treated with Orinase. This idea did not work out; in fact, no simple test for picking out Orinase-responsive diabetics has been found. But two young physicians, Drs. Roger H. Unger and Leonard L. Madison of the University of Texas, seized upon injectable Orinase for something that may prove far more valuable—a simple, reliable, quick test for *diagnosing* diabetes, especially early, mild cases of the disease.

During the past several decades, physicians have been searching constantly for a reliable test for diabetes. The difficulty is that the familiar blood- and urinary-sugar tests are not always reliable. Blood-sugar levels may not be high, under the conditions of the usual blood-sugar test, until late in the disease; and mild diabetics particularly may not spill sugar in the urine. Early diagnosis of diabetes is vital, in order to prevent the severe damage uncontrolled, advanced diabetes can do to many parts of the body.

In an effort to detect early diabetes, medical men have

made use of a procedure known as the glucose-tolerance test. In this, the patient is given a large dose of sugar (either by mouth or by injection); if his blood-sugar level rises to excessive levels and is unduly slow to return to normal, he is presumed to have diabetes. Unfortunately, the glucose-tolerance test takes several hours, is often uncomfortable for the patient, and is frequently difficult to interpret. Even with great care, it may easily attach a false diabetes label to normal individuals—a serious matter because (to mention just one penalty of the disease) diabetics must pay extra for life insurance, when they can obtain life insurance at all.

Drs. Unger and Madison recalled an observation made by Dr. Mirsky at the University of Pittsburgh in one of the first studies of Orinase. Dr. Mirsky had found that Orinase produces a much swifter fall of blood sugar in normal individuals than in moderately severe diabetics. Now, the Texas physicians took blood samples from 100 suitably prepared nondiabetic individuals and 79 patients with mild diabetes. Each was then given an injection of 1 gram of Orinase, and blood samples were taken at twenty, thirty, forty, and sixty minutes later.

Blood-sugar measurements upon the various blood samples revealed a dramatic difference in response to Orinase. The blood-sugar levels of the nondiabetics dropped rapidly, hitting "bottom" thirty minutes after the dose of Orinase. In the diabetic group, the fall was much slower; the fall actually did not reach a maximum during the one-hour period of the test. The best separation of diabetics from nondiabetics occurred in the twenty-minute blood samples. In 96 per cent of the nondiabetics, the twenty-minute blood sugar fell to below 84 per cent of the value before the test; in 94 per cent of the diabetics, the blood sugar remained at 84 per cent or higher. Only 5 per cent of the entire group could not be clearly classified as diabetic or nondiabetic on the basis of the twenty-minute blood-sugar level. Thus, Orinase may well lead to the development of a new, easily performed test for diabetes.

At the present moment, it is still too early to assess the full range of possibilities opened up by Orinase. But two are particularly interesting, though their practical application may belong to the future. One is the possibility of diagnosing diabetes at a very early stage when, recent research suggests, treatment with an agent like Orinase may actually be able to restore the patient to normal. The other is diagnosis of mild diabetes during pregnancy and prevention of the stillbirths and other fetal abnormalities that often seem to accompany untreated diabetes during pregnancy.

Let us take these up one at a time. Over the years, a good many physicians have made it a practice, whenever possible, to test blood relatives of known diabetics for diabetes. An abundance of evidence has long made it clear that a predisposition to the disease is inherited. In fact, by screening relatives of diabetics, physicians have uncovered many patients with so-called occult forms of the disease—individuals who were definitely diabetic, but had not yet developed the severe thirst, the weight loss, and other symptoms that drive the "frank" diabetic to the doctor.

The discovery of such cases of occult diabetes has served two purposes. First, it has helped the individuals involved by putting them under the care of a physician at a stage when much could be done to control the disease by diet alone and before the appearance of the many serious complications—such as diabetic acidosis, blood-vessel disease, kidney disease, and blindness—that beset and shorten the life of the untreated diabetic. In the promptly and properly treated diabetic, such complications may often be postponed for long periods of time.

Second, the identification of occult diabetics has made it clear that maturity-onset diabetes especially is a disease with a long history. Patients can have hidden "prediabetic" abnormalities five, ten, twenty years, or perhaps even longer before development of weight loss, excessive thirst, excessive urination, and other symptoms of full-blown diabetes.

Shortly after Orinase was released for general medical use, two of the investigators who had worked with it from the earliest days, Drs. Stefan S. Fajans and Jerome W. Conn of the University of Michigan, decided to try the new antidiabetic in patients with very mild early diabetes. Such patients have hitherto been treated mainly by diet and weight control. Since they are still able to produce much insulin on their own, most physicians consider it unwise to subject them to the risks and encumbrances of insulin therapy. Some specialists feel, in fact, that insulin therapy might do harm by suppressing the patient's own production of the hormone. Drs. Fajans and Conn were anxious to see whether something might be accomplished for the mild, early diabetic by long-term treatment with Orinase.

Twelve patients were selected for the trial. All had been given glucose-tolerance tests because of a strong family history of diabetes. All twelve had been found to have a diabetic response to the test, although they had no other symptoms of diabetes. Also, the patients were relatively young—the age range was eleven to thirty-five years—for the type of diabetes they had; but this was doubtless a result of the discovery of their disease before it had a chance to appear as overt diabetes.

The twelve were placed on appropriate, moderately restricted diets and instructed to take a gram of Orinase a day. At intervals of two to four months, each member of the group stopped taking Orinase for one to two days (to allow elimination of the drug from their systems) and came in for a glucose-tolerance test.

In one patient—whose diabetes had actually been known for five years and who thus was perhaps not so early a case as the others—there was no improvement in the glucose-tolerance test. Orinase had kept his diabetes under good control, but there was no sign that the disease itself was improving.

In five other patients, glucose tolerance improved considerably after three to ten months of Orinase. And in six of the twelve, the response to the glucose-tolerance test returned all the way to normal (though a very sensitive modification of the test carried out with the aid of cortisone still showed some abnormalities). In two of these six patients, Orinase treatment was suspended after the standard glucose-tolerance tests became normal. One of the two patients still had a normal test response three months later. The response of the other remained normal for five months without Orinase, before it again became abnormal.

Patients with diabetes occasionally appear to improve spontaneously, but these improvements are generally the result of other changes in the economy of the body and are almost invariably purely temporary. No such consistent trend toward the amelioration of diabetes had ever occurred with any previous method of treatment. Much further study will be required by many investigators to rule out any possibility of spontaneous remissions or chance variations in the glucose-tolerance test in Drs. Fajans and Conn's patients. But when the University of Michigan researchers described their results at a meeting of the American Diabetes Association in June, 1959, more than one diabetes expert called their report "one of the most hopeful to come out of diabetes research in years." For the first time, there is hope (particularly with the help of injectable Orinase for detecting early diabetes) that the development of full-blown diabetes can be prevented in many patients by prophylactic treatment with Orinase.

So much for the possibility of reversing mild diabetes and preventing the development of more advanced forms of the disease. One of the sad and puzzling features of diabetes is that women with uncontrolled disease often miscarry or give birth to abnormally large infants, many of which are stillborn. The incidence of congenital defects is also higher than usual among the children of diabetic mothers. No one understands just why this is so. But every obstetrician and diabetes specialist knows also that the only way to save the diabetic woman's baby is to control her diabetes carefully during pregnancy and to provide both the mother and infant with other special care.

Since many cases of diabetes develop gradually over a period of time, a number of physicians began wondering some years ago whether early, unsuspected diabetes might be involved in some of the difficulties of supposedly nondiabetic women. Several men set out to investigate the question, among them Dr. W. P. U. Jackson of the University of Cape Town, South Africa.

Dr. Jackson proceeded in what must seem by now the familiar way. He performed glucose-tolerance tests upon pregnant or recently pregnant women with a family history of diabetes or who were for other reasons under suspicion as possibly diabetic. He then followed up those with an abnormal response to the test. Their infants—both those born then and in succeeding pregnancies—were likewise followed up.

By 1955, he had enough cases so that there could be little doubt of the findings. Most of the women with an abnormal response to the glucose-tolerance test had already become plainly diabetic, and the others did so in the following years. Equally important, even before the development of overt diabetes, most of the babies borne by the women proved abnormally large, and very nearly half were stillborn or died soon after birth.

Dr. Jackson decided to treat prediabetic mothers in the same way overtly diabetic pregnant women are managed. He put them on diets low in carbohydrate. Labor was induced early, before the fetus grew too large. The babies were treated as premature infants. What happened in his first several cases as a result is best described in a report made by Dr. Jackson and a colleague, N. Woolf, in the British medical journal *Lancet* in 1957.

> Six of our mothers already diagnosed as prediabetic have recently had children, all living, including one set of twins.... All were induced early, despite which all the babies were on the large side. The previous pregnancies in

three of these mothers had produced stillbirths. Two further mothers, suspected of having prediabetes, did not return to see us when they again fell pregnant, and both produced stillbirths. We believe we save babies.

During the same period and later, investigators in other centers were similarly finding an association between maternal prediabetes and abnormal pregnancies (though not all found quite so high an incidence of oversized fetuses as Dr. Jackson). And several were also treating prediabetic mothers as though diabetic, with results as gratifying, in terms of babies saved, as those obtained by the Cape Town physician. Among those who carried out these several studies were Dr. J. P. Hoet of Brussels; Dr. Hugh Wilkerson of the U.S. Public Health Service diabetes field unit in Boston; Dr. H. C. Miller of Boston; and Dr. F. D. Lukens of the University of Pennsylvania.

There are no reliable estimates to show how great a contribution unsuspected prediabetes (really early, mild diabetes) is making to the over-all incidence of miscarriage, stillbirth, congenital defect, and neonatal death. But it must be sizable, for diabetes is a common disease—there are 1.5 million known diabetics in the United States—and early, asymptomatic diabetes must be frequent, too. Many prediabetic women, furthermore, must be of childbearing age.

Thus, early, unidentified diabetes may be a substantial problem of the very beginning as well as the later years of life. If so, hope of a solution may lie with means of finding and treating the mother with an agent like Orinase.

Several years after its introduction, Orinase continues to occupy a nearly unique place in the treatment of diabetes.

Insulin and diet continue to be of great importance. For example, whether or not insulin or Orinase is prescribed, diabetics are almost always placed on diets to minimize carbohydrate intake or to bring about a weight loss (many diabetics are overweight in early stages of the disease) or both. Insulin is required not only by diabetics unable to produce an adequate supply of their own, but by many other diabetics during times of stress (other illnesses, surgical operations, and so forth). At the end of 1959, however, Orinase was being taken daily by more than 1 in every 3 known United States diabetics—about 600,000 in all.

Several other oral antidiabetics have appeared. BZ-55 itself is in decreasing use in Europe and was never placed on sale in the United States. Its American manufacturer, Eli Lilly & Co., withdrew it—without any prodding from government or other agencies—when clinical tests disclosed serious toxicity. Also, both Upjohn and Lilly later voluntarily withdrew an experimental oral antidiabetic, metahexamide, for the same reason. (Metahexamide had seemed especially promising. Animal tests indicated it to be quite safe. A sulfonylurea, it was far more potent, weight for weight, in lowering blood sugar than either BZ-55 or Orinase.)

A place in medicine has been won by a number of other new oral antidiabetics. But none has been able to match the remarkable safety or position of the drug that turned up when researchers finally gave notice to what was right under their noses.

13 | The Many Sides of Modern Pharmaceutical Research

Since 1913, when Dr. Frederick Heyl came to Upjohn as chief chemist, profound changes have taken place in research activities at Upjohn. The change is not simply a matter of size, though Upjohn research has grown greatly—from 3 employees to 550 in the research laboratories proper and another 150 in chemical, pharmaceutical, and fermentation development work; from a basement laboratory with a few pieces of glassware to elaborately equipped laboratories (there is even an atom smasher for experimental electron-beam sterilization of drugs) occupying most of the buildings downtown and with outposts at Portage Road; from an annual budget of a few tens of thousands of dollars to one of $15 million. The decisive change was in the nature of the research and the role of research in the company as a whole.

As in the case of the men who were joining the staffs of other pharmaceutical houses at the time, when Dr. Heyl was hired by Upjohn, his primary task was in the area of "control." He was expected to develop laboratory tests to check the quality and uniformity of Upjohn products and assure their conformity with the food and drug law. He also hoped to do research on new products. But note the word *also;* control procedures were his major responsibility. Moreover, the new products which he had in mind were chiefly improvements in known drugs. In 1913, no one thought in terms of searching systematically for entirely new drugs.

Laboratory testing of products continues to be an essential part of pharmaceutical manufacturing. In the Upjohn Company, however, control is no longer the responsibility of the research division (though it is under the over-all supervision of the company's top research man, Dr. Schreiber, who is also the company's vice-president for scientific administration). The control laboratories have their own staffs and the research laboratories have gone on to other tasks. As the research chronicles in previous chapters indicate, Upjohn research has moved progressively into a new realm in which new drugs are aggressively sought by all possible means, including creation in the chemical laboratory.

Not all Upjohn products stem from the Kalamazoo company's own research. Some, like Orinase, are manufactured under license from other pharmaceutical firms. Numerous others make use of process steps or similar know-how originated in other laboratories. All rest on the broad base of the vast and growing body of modern scientific knowledge—a body of knowledge open to all with the patience and skill to take advantage of it. Nevertheless, the greatest part of the Upjohn Company's current output is of products developed in its own laboratories.

Upjohn is widely considered to have one of the most substantial and effective research establishments in the pharmaceutical industry—indeed, in any industrial company in the United States. Its size and scope raise important, intriguing questions with a direct bearing not only on the course of the Upjohn Company, but on many aspects of contemporary science as a whole.

Let us begin with a glance at the over-all organization of research and development in the Kalamazoo pharmaceutical firm and the fields in which it has research currently under way. To begin with, new drugs must first be discovered and studied in animals; their worth must then be determined in patients, and finally, methods of manufacturing them in quantity and of putting them into a dosage form suitable for everyday medical use must be found. At Upjohn, separate organizational units carry out these tasks. Most basic research is conducted by the chemical and biological research divisions. Clinical trial is carried out through a clinical investigation group, which arranges for trials of new Upjohn products in leading hospitals and medical centers. Manufacturing methods and development of dosage forms is the province of several research and development groups attached to the company's manufacturing division. In this chapter, we will take a look at chemical and biological research activities; clinical investigation and manufacturing and product development will be examined later.

Pharmaceutical firms that manufacture a limited number of products—"specialty houses" in the language of the industry—generally limit their research to the areas they are interested in. Most specialty houses are small or medium-sized firms and could hardly afford to do otherwise. Long-line firms like Upjohn, on the other hand, are compelled to carry on a very great variety of studies.

In fact, at the beginning of 1960, Upjohn investigators were at work in almost all major areas of current interest in biology and medicine. For instance, there were groups engaged in studies both of diabetes itself and of possible new agents (prepared by other Upjohn researchers) for treating diabetes. Another sizable force of researchers was preparing new steroid hormonal compounds for colleagues to test in animals, while yet other research men were carrying on basic studies of some of the diseases the new steroids might be employed in. Pituitary hormones were the concern of still another group. A large research task force was searching soil samples for antibiotics active against viruses as well as bacteria and fungi. The attack against infectious organisms was also being pressed through fundamental studies of virus metabolism, the formation of cell walls in bacteria, and the like.

Another subject under close scrutiny in the complex of buildings in downtown Kalamazoo was the fate of fats in the body—how fats are broken down and how built up—because of the close connection between fat metabolism and the great medical problems of overweight and coronary heart disease. Protein chemistry was a subject of study, too. And so was the mechanism by which foods, drugs, and other substances are absorbed into the system through the walls of the stomach and small intestine. A number of Upjohn scientists had become dissatisfied with what was known about the absorption of orally administered drugs; a fundamental study of digestive tract absorption mechanisms was the result.

More effective drugs were being sought for peptic ulcer, high blood pressure, and mental illness. A multipronged attack on cancer was under way. As part of the National Cancer Chemotherapy Screening Program, steroid compounds and antibiotic broths were being tested against animal cancers and also—by a screening technique originated by Upjohn researchers—against human cancers grown in tissue culture. Other staff scientists were conducting immunological studies of cancer, with the hope of finding immunological means of preventing or destroying tumors. And, inevitably, there was much work under way on the mode of action and possible toxic effects of drugs under consideration for clinical trial.

There has even been research on vaccines, although Upjohn left the vaccine field a decade ago. A few years ago, a tissue culture laboratory was added to the research division's facilities, because of its value in studies of viruses and antiviral agents and also in the study of cancer. Two promising experimental measles vaccines were developed in the course of the tissue culture work; they were licensed to another firm. Finally, the Upjohn Company was also supporting a substantial volume of research in chemistry, biology, and medicine through grants to investigators in universities.

Research in industrial laboratories is often criticized as being chiefly applied rather than basic research, i.e., as aimed too much at the development of specific products and not enough at the addition of new information to man's stockpile of scientific knowledge. Like a number of other large pharmaceutical houses, however, the Upjohn Company clearly takes a broad view of the kind of research its staff scientists ought to do. A good deal of the work carried on in its laboratories is not oriented toward specific products. There is the hope, of course, that it will benefit the company in some way. Thus, the study of virus metabolism could conceivably lead to an agent useful in the treatment of virus disease, and research on stomach and intestinal absorption could result in the improvement of numerous medicinal products. But these and many other current Upjohn studies are certainly not product-development projects; they are basic research.

In conducting its research program, the Kalamazoo pharmaceutical company is guided by three underlying considerations. The first is the necessity of providing a steady flow of new, improved products. In an era of rapid scientific and technical advance, a pharmaceutical firm that fails to develop new products can expect only a decline in sales, for competitors will certainly market the improved products it ignores. Many recent products, such as several of the antibiotics, have had no more than a year or two of substantial sale before being superseded.

A second basic consideration in shaping Upjohn research is the dual need to enlarge the company's experience and competence in areas in which it is active and to acquire experience in areas that may become commercially important in future. There is always the chance that it will be an Upjohn researcher who makes the discovery opening up the new area. If the discovery is actually made by someone else, the company will at least have essential know-how and perhaps patents that will prevent exclusion from the new field.

The third consideration is that research, even upon a single medical or scientific problem, has its best chance of success from a many-pronged attack. There is never certainty of success in research, no guarantee that the rainbow can be climbed to the pot of gold beyond, no matter how a research problem is approached. Suppose, though, that Upjohn research had chosen to put all its eggs in one basket and follow one approach only (instead of seven) in research on methods of producing cortical hormones. The eggs could easily have been put in the wrong basket—into one of the approaches that had no useful result.

So far, we have had a glimpse of the over-all size of the Upjohn research establishment, some of the areas it is active in, and a few guiding policies. But we have not really seen how the machine works. How does a pharmaceutical laboratory like Upjohn's go about finding and developing new drugs?

Like their university colleagues, many of the scientists on the staff of the Upjohn research laboratories are skeptical of the value of some applications of one of the favorite research devices of the present day—the procedure called "screening." In screening, large numbers of chemical compounds or other substances are tested in animals or by some other laboratory procedure to uncover substances with useful medical effects (for instance, antibiotics active against particular varieties of bacteria). In some major diseases, the chances of obtaining useful drugs by screening are felt to be small because no one really knows what type of chemical to test or how to test for a drug that might be effective in that particular disease. This is one reason why progressive pharmaceutical companies take part in basic studies of many diseases. Such research sometimes represents the most reasonable avenue to an advance in treatment.

Screening programs have nevertheless proved of great value in important areas of medical research and are carried out on a large scale in government and other laboratories as well as by the pharmaceutical industry. Numerous useful drugs have been uncovered with their aid; among others, the list includes antibiotics, sulfonamides, antimalarials, anticonvulsives (for treating epilepsy), tranquilizers. An additional attraction, which no pharmaceutical company can ignore, is the fact that better patent protection can be obtained under United States law for synthetic chemicals and antibiotic products than for a product like, say, a natural hormone. For all these reasons, therefore, a sizable part of the Upjohn research staff is engaged in preparing and screening new chemical compounds and antibiotic broths. New chemical compounds of different types have recently been synthesized and screened at Upjohn at a rate of some fifteen hundred a year. The number of soil samples and similar "raw materials" screened for antibiotics is even greater (because it is easier to test a soil sample for antibiotic activity than to synthesize a new chemical)—about forty thousand a year. In addition, many natural substances are screened for possible usefulness in medicine.

The screening technique depends on what is being screened and what for. Antibiotic samples may be screened against cultures of bacteria, fungi, viruses, or—as part of the National Cancer Chemotherapy Screening Program—their ability to destroy cancers of several kinds under various circumstances. Chemicals with possible hormone activity are tested in laboratory animals of several species. Compounds for the treatment of diabetes, high blood pressure, peptic ulcer, and other ills are likewise tested in a variety of animals, including (when appropriate and possible) animals with a laboratory equivalent of the disease in question.

Finding evidence of interesting biological or medical activity in a compound or antibiotic broth is actually but the first step toward the development of a new medicinal agent. Promising compounds are put through many other studies to confirm and extend the evidence of useful activity and to learn as much as possible about their mode of action. Most important, their toxicity will be checked. Later, if a compound or antibiotic seems promising enough for trial in man, still more extensive animal studies will be carried out. Long-term as well as acute toxicity will be measured. An effort will be made to trace the compound through the animal's body and determine just where it goes and whether and how it is excreted. Other appropriate studies will likewise be done; thus, an antibiotic for treating bacterial diseases will be put through special procedures to see whether bacteria become resistant to it. Such data is not only needed to tell Upjohn investigators whether the drug is likely to be useful, but will be required for the New Drug Application that must be filed with the Food and Drug Administration before any new drug is placed on sale.

One of the problems calling for nice judgement is the question of which drugs to try in man. There can be no hard and fast "maximum toxicity" or "minimum effectiveness" rules, for the ailments of man and the means of treating them are too varied. A drug with a considerable risk of toxic reactions is worth trial in a fatal disease for which there is no other effective treatment. A low level of toxicity is mandatory when safe means of treatment exist. In general, a new drug will be selected for trial in man only if it promises to be more effective and no more toxic than comparable drugs already in use, or as effective but safer, or both safer and more effective.

In any event, the number of drugs that pass successfully through the laboratory screening and testing process is very small. Fewer than ten antibiotics worthy of clinical trial were found among the 200,000 or so soil culture isolates screened in the Upjohn laboratories between 1954 and 1959 (and only one—Albamycin—finally emerged as a major product). The mortality among new synthetic chemical compounds is also extremely high. Out of the 15,000-odd new compounds prepared by Upjohn chemists and put through laboratory tests in the past decade (at a cost that may go well into the thousands of dollars for a single compound), only a few dozen have been passed on to clinical investigators; and only a small proportion of the drugs tested clinically survived to reach the market.

Until a generation or so ago, the phrase "scientific administration" generally meant the management of a laboratory's business affairs: the writing of pay checks, the purchase of supplies, the hiring of a handful of secretaries. The growth of large laboratories and institutes with highly organized research programs during and since World War II has given the phrase a vexing new meaning. Now it refers to the making of scientific policy and the direction of the scientific activities of the laboratory staff—a vastly more difficult task.

The large laboratory derives an advantage from the fact that it is able to mobilize large teams of scientists and technicians for specific projects. The development of atomic bombs and the first earth satellites are spectacular examples of what the organized scientific task force can accomplish; the pharmaceutical industry itself can furnish many more, from the development of the sulfa drugs and penicillin forward. Ideas, though, are the real key to progress and history has shown again and again that many of the most original and fruitful ideas arise in the heads of individuals who are not trying to zero in on a team target. How, then, does one manage a large research laboratory so as to obtain the benefits of programmed team research without destroying the opportunity for individual ideas?

In the case of a large pharmaceutical laboratory, the problem is compounded by two other seemingly mutually exclusive requirements. The laboratory's efforts must be spread over most or all areas of current or potential interest to the company. But every problem taken up ought to be investigated with the utmost thoroughness. Suppose compounds are being screened in a search for a drug for disease X; they might also be useful in Y or Z or still another disease; hence, they should be screened for such activity and for all other possibly useful types of biological activity, too. And intermediate and by-product compounds should be tested in the same way. The valuable antifungal antibiotic griseofulvin, recently developed in England, remained undiscovered for two decades because no one thought to test penicillin cultures (in which griseofulvin occurs) for antifungal activity.

The conflict between wide coverage and complete exploration of each particular research undertaking and its ramifications is easily resolved only in an infinitely large laboratory, with an unlimited reserve of scientists to pursue every new possibility that comes up. An infinitely large laboratory might also ease, if not resolve, the team versus individual research conflict. It would have plenty of scientists for both kinds of research. A real laboratory, like that of the Upjohn Company, must make compromises.

Upjohn research is organized into nearly a dozen and a half units grouped into chemical research (with the primary responsibility for preparing new chemical compounds and screening for antibiotics) and biological research (responsible for laboratory testing of new compounds and antibiotics and for basic biological and medical research). A separate veterinary research division has its field headquarters at the company's research farm outside Kalamazoo. As a result of the laboratory's growth, Upjohn's over-all research chief, Dr. Schreiber, vice-president for scientific administration, now has under him separate directors of chemical and biological research. (They are, respectively, Dr. David I. Weisblat, the Ohio-born and Ohio State University–trained chemist who devised Upjohn's folic acid synthesis process, and Dr. Robert W. Heinle, also Ohio-born and a medical graduate and former associate professor at Western Reserve University Medical School.)

The basic research unit is the team, often made up of researchers from several departments to bring the knowledge of specialists in different sciences to bear on a research problem. Most research groups consist of three or four scientists and their laboratory assistants. However, the policy is flexible. Large teams have been at work in such key areas to the Kalamazoo pharmaceutical company as steroid hormones and antibiotics. Special task forces have been mobilized for "fire-engine jobs" to follow up major developments—with the research directors hoping that nothing important is being missed meanwhile in other areas.

Dr. Schreiber would personally prefer to see smaller research groups and even more individual researchers at work in areas where that is possible. He feels that such an arrangement might be more productive of new ideas. In the meantime, though, Upjohn research has a handy device for encouraging individual research enterprise and new ideas. Every staff scientist is permitted to spend 10 to 20 per cent of his work week on a research problem of his own choosing. The only limitation upon what may be done is that it shall be in an area of general interest to the company—a limitation more apparent than real because most Upjohn researchers' scientific interests are in chemistry, biology, or medicine, or they would not be working for a pharmaceutical manufacturer.

Many pharmaceutical firms have a similar free time for research policy. For Upjohn, it has been a significant factor—along with the excellent scientific library and laboratory facilities, plus the company's general character as an employer—in bringing able young scientists into the Upjohn research organization. In addition, free-time research has been a significant source of new ideas. "It's surprising," says one of the research directors, "how many of the projects taken up by our people in their free time develop in six months or a year to the point where they are taken over as regularly assigned projects." Perhaps, in the free time for research policy, pharmaceutical companies like Upjohn have the nucleus of a scheme for keeping individual research alive in an age in which the team seems to have taken over almost all of science.

14 | The Critical Test

More than a century ago, the French physiologist Claude Bernard pointed out that there can be no progress in medicine without experiments on human beings. "Experiments made on man," he said, "are always the most decisive." Bernard's observation follows from man's uniqueness. There are many resemblances between us and our fellow creatures, but there are numerous differences, too, just as every species of animal differs from every other. As a consequence, no medical treatment can be studied in animals alone. No matter how thorough the animal studies, surprises will still occur when a new treatment is tried in human patients. A method of treating human illness can therefore be said to work only when it has been tried and found effective in man himself.

The need for human tests is particularly urgent in ailments in which mental and emotional reactions play a direct or indirect part.

During this generation of express-train-swift advance in medicine, the testing of new drugs and methods of treatment has mushroomed into what amounts to the new medical specialty of clinical investigation. The art of clinical investigation has, of course, been practiced since the earliest times. Any physician who makes a new observation upon a patient or tries a new treatment is a clinical investigator. Hippocrates, the father of Greek medicine (and whoever else may have contributed to the vast body of medical observations known as the Hippocratic writings) was a clinical investigator, and a good one. But recent years have begun to bring specialized techniques to the testing of new methods of treatment, just as the modern era has brought specialization to other areas of science and medicine.

A major force in the growth of clinical investigation has been the expansion of pharmaceutical research. Drug manufacturers have had an increasing number of experimental medicinal agents to be tested in man. Although members of the medical department of one large drug firm do staff a part of the community hospital in their firm's home city in order to keep their hands in as physicians, pharmaceutical companies do not have patients. Doctors do. The result has been an informal, but increasingly significant, working relationship between the pharmaceutical industry and several thousand physicians with an interest in clinical trial of new drugs.

In the case of the Upjohn Company, arrangements for new-drug trials are handled through the clinical investigation section of the medical division. Now nearly twenty-five years old, the medical division has a dozen and a half physicians on its staff and several vitally important functions, including the preparation of New Drug Applications for the Food and Drug Administration (of which more later), the writing of product literature, keeping up with trends in medicine, and answering the many questions practicing physicians address to pharmaceutical companies pertaining to their products. But no function of a pharmaceutical company's medical staff is more critical than arranging for tests of the company's new products in human patients.

The evaluation of new drugs in man is usually divided into three phases. In the first, supplies of the drug, plus financial grants if special research costs are involved, are given to a small circle of clinical investigators. These physicians administer the drug with great caution to carefully selected patients in order, first, to confirm the useful effects found in the animal laboratory and, second, to make sure that the drug is safe enough (as the animal studies had indicated it would be, or it would never have been submitted to clinical trial). The patients are watched closely for signs of toxicity. Whenever feasible, special studies are done to follow the drug through the patient's body. Studies may also be carried out in healthy volunteers. Meanwhile, and throughout critical phases of the trial, investigation of the drug in laboratory animals continues back in Upjohn's biological research division.

Dr. Harold F. Hailman, the head of the clinical investigation section—a double-degree man from the University of Illinois (M.D. plus Ph.D. in physiology)—and his colleagues try to draw first-phase investigators chiefly from medical schools and teaching hospitals. Members of medical school and teaching hospital staffs are usually more experienced in research than physicians in smaller centers or in private practice. Moreover, their opinions carry greater weight with the medical profession.

But the evaluation of a drug cannot be carried out solely by medical school investigators. Neither the schools nor their patients are typical of medical practice as a whole. Medical schools often have an unusually large proportion of very sick patients referred from smaller hospitals; the care provided is also more elaborate. Consequently, it is necessary to go to physicians outside the medical schools for trial of new drugs under more ordinary conditions.

This is done in the so-called second phase of new-drug evaluation, a stage undertaken only after first-phase studies are far enough along to show that the drug does have useful effects in human disease and to bring out any hazards in its use. Once this is accomplished, arrangements for additional tests are made with a larger group of physicians, including a sizable number in private practice.

When a clinical researcher is asked by a responsible pharmaceutical firm to test a new drug, it is understood that he may or may not, as he wishes, publish his findings, whether favorable or unfavorable, in a medical journal. The pharmacuetical company does ask, though, that it be kept informed of the progress of the trial. This is needed not only for the decision as to whether to put the drug into production and on sale, but for the writing of informational literature for physicians who will use the drug and for the compilation of data required by the Food and Drug Administration.

The third phase in the clinical evaluation of a new drug begins after the drug has gone on general sale, and it really represents a continuation of previous clinical research with the drug. Responsible pharmaceutical manufacturers continue to sponsor such research on their products, instead of cutting it off when they go on sale, for many reasons. One is to have as early a warning as possible should problems arise with the drug; unexpected difficulties can occur even after the most thorough preliminary clinical trial. A second reason is the hope of learning as much about the drug as possible. This can lead both to better drugs and to new uses for the drug itself.

Upjohn has been the beneficiary more than once of research carried out after a drug went on sale and the preliminary clinical trial was presumably over. The exciting discovery that treatment of very early, mild diabetes with Orinase may result in remissions of the disease was made long after Orinase was licensed and had gone on sale. And late last year, clinical investigators found an important new application for Medrol, the anti-inflammatory steroid introduced by Upjohn in 1956. Persons with heart disease and other patients taking diuretic drugs in order to eliminate excess fluid from their bodies often become resistant to diuretics. Clinical investigators have found that treatment with Medrol frequently restores the effectiveness of diuretics. As yet, why Medrol and some related compounds have this effect is not wholly clear. But Medrol does have this effect—a benefit for both patients and the Upjohn Company derived from clinical research.

Although careful clinical trials would be conducted by responsible pharmaceutical manufacturers in any event, one of the main concerns of the clinical investigation department in a United States pharmaceutical firm is meeting legal requirements for new drugs. Under the Food, Drug, and Cosmetic Act passed by Congress in 1938 and other Federal laws and regulations, what amounts to a license must be obtained for any new drug. The Public Health Service—as everyone learned during the Salk vaccine mess—has responsibility for licensing vaccines and a number of other biological products; PHS also certifies each batch of the vaccines and drugs under its control. Other drugs are under the jurisdiction of the FDA. One FDA duty is to certify batches of penicillin, streptomycin, and several other antibiotics. In addition, the FDA is responsible for the "licensing" of all new drugs not otherwise covered—which means not only genuinely new drugs but may mean any new variations upon, or mixture of, drugs already in use, even drugs in use for centuries, if the new use is not generally known to be safe. So pharmaceutical manufacturers developing new drugs must deal with the PHS and the FDA, though much more often the FDA—a circumstance that has imposed legal as well as technical burdens on the drug industry. It is a curious fact that the Food, Drug, and Cosmetic Act not only caused an expansion of laboratories for testing drugs for safety. Many pharmaceutical legal departments also date from the act. This is the case with Upjohn. Leslie D. Harrop was brought into the company as its first general counsel shortly after the act was passed.

Technically, the FDA does not issue licenses for new drugs. What happens is this: A manufacturer wishing to market a new drug files a New Drug Application setting forth required information pertinent to the drug. He tells how it is made and submits proof that it meets an appropriate standard of safety. (A considerable risk of toxicity is permissible in a drug effective in a fatal disease for which there is no other useful treatment. Drugs for ailments of little consequence or for diseases for which there are already safe remedies must be very safe.) If two or more companies wish to manufacture the same new drug, each must file an NDA and prove its own product safe. Thus, when Upjohn began to market its own brand of cortisone, the Kalamazoo company had to file an NDA, though Merck & Company, the first cortisone manufacturer, had already done so. If the FDA makes no objection to an NDA within sixty days, the NDA automatically "becomes effective" (as drug industry men say) and the new drug may be placed on sale.

It should be noted that a new drug need not be proved effective in order to be licensed. When the Food, Drug, and Cosmetic Act was on its way through Congress, there were people who argued that manufacturers should be required to prove the effectiveness as well as the safety of new drugs before they were allowed to go on sale. No such provision was written into the law. If it had been, the FDA, the pharmaceutical industry, and the entire profession of medicine would soon have been bogged in helpless debate, for the effectiveness of a drug can be extremely difficult to define or measure. And, as mentioned earlier, valuable new applications for drugs frequently turn up after a drug first comes into use. A "prove-effectiveness-first" rule could easily bar useful drugs. The FDA, however, exercises close supervision over the claims that may be made for a drug on the label and literature accompanying the package. And effectiveness is a factor in determining the standard of safety a drug must meet.

In the past, virtually all the data on the actions and effects of Upjohn medicinals in man has come from outside investigators and laboratories. About a year ago, though, the medical division was equipped with a small laboratory of its own. In addition, a modest program of studies was organized among volunteers from the staff of a local hospital and among prisoners in a Michigan penitentiary. (All volunteers are paid and the prisoners are particularly eager to take part; the research projects relieve the tedium of jail.) The purpose of the clinical investigation laboratory and the volunteer program is to obtain systematic, reliable data on such questions as the blood levels produced in man by doses of various antibiotics, and the like. Experience had shown that it was not always possible to secure complete data of this kind as quickly as needed from outside researchers.

The new activities of the Upjohn clinical investigation unit are a reflection of the fact that clinical evaluation of new drugs is becoming both more elaborate and more sophisticated. In recent years, the standards and proofs of safety demanded by the FDA before new drugs are allowed on sale have become progressively higher and more stringent. More detailed studies of drug actions and effects, both in animals and man, are called for, and larger, better-controlled series of clinical cases.

The Kalamazoo pharmaceutical firm's research and clinical investigation specialists have likewise been anxious to improve the testing of new Upjohn products. For one thing, skillfully conducted trials have a better chance of yielding results quickly. They should reveal serious objections to the use of a drug sooner—and thereby save the cost of producing and arranging to market a drug that might have to be withdrawn. They should single out swiftly a really superior and valuable new product—and so accelerate its introduction into wide use. (Pharmaceutical products, it should be remembered, help sick people as well as earn money for pharmaceutical manufacturers.)

But several difficulties have arisen to make the testing of new drugs a taxing and often baffling problem. To begin with, conscientious pharmaceutical researchers would like results that are completely objective and free of bias. In the long run, the surest and shortest road to success in the pharmaceutical business is to have a genuinely effective drug whose value is manifest year after year. Thus, outstandingly successful Upjohn products have benefited greatly from effective promotion by the Upjohn sales department, but first they were good drugs. Unhappily, it is not easy to be sure that the results obtained with a drug are due to the drug and not to natural variations in the course of a disease, biased selection of patients (giving a new drug to patients who would get better regardless of treatment, and so forth), or the enthusiasm of doctors or patients. The history of medicine and the pharmaceutical industry is replete with instances of drugs and treatments that started out like a house afire, only to fizzle out like a wet match. Conversely, good and useful drugs may well have been killed by incompetent testing (though no one knows their names, because drugs tagged as failures in an early stage of testing sink quickly out of sight).

In an effort to avoid such difficulties, many new procedures have been introduced into clinical testing. Most important has been the controlled trial, in which patients are divided into two groups as closely alike as possible, except that one receives the new drug or treatment and the other does not. In a further effort to eliminate researchers' and patients' emotional reactions and so assure trustworthy results, controlled trials are often arranged on the so-called double-blind pattern, with neither the patients nor the doctors who administer the drug or assess the results knowing until the test is over what kind of treatment any patient received. But even double-blind trials can be misleading. A doctor's enthusiasm for a new drug can make both the drug on trial and a dummy product used for purposes of comparison appear more effective than they actually are. A physician's skepticism can similarly be communicated to patients in a double-blind trial and make both useful and dummy drugs seem of little use. In either case, the outcome of an elaborately planned, costly trial is frustratingly inconclusive.

It seems that there is no device for mechanically cranking out reliable results in a clinical trial and that much depends on the experience and good judgment of the clinical researcher. In the past decade, though, the supply of new drugs awaiting test has considerably outrun the supply of experienced testers. This is due in part to the newness of many specialized clinical testing techniques, in part to the fact that a clinical investigator does not have quite the same function as a physician. The physician's sole concern is necessarily and properly the welfare of the patient in front of him. The clinical investigator has to take a rather different view. He is concerned with the individual patient's welfare, too, as evidenced by the careful precautions the good investigator takes to assure the patient's safety. But he is also concerned with the value of a treatment for the whole world of patients. To measure its effectiveness, he must sometimes (with the patients' consent) give the treatment to some of his patients only.

The split between physician and investigative scientist has troubled medicine throughout history. It has simply become more acute than in the past because of rapid progress in basic medical research and because of the inevitable lag in training people in a newly expanded field. Thoughtful research men are fearful that the shortage may cause the overlooking and loss of drugs that might save lives.

"I keep thinking of the more than a million compounds chemists throughout the world have synthesized," says one of Upjohn's senior clinical investigators, "and the 1,500 new ones a year our own chemists are turning out. Most of them are sitting on the shelf labeled useless. But are they? DDT sat on a shelf for sixty years before a use for it was found. Isoniazid spent years on the shelf before anyone knew of its immense value in tuberculosis.

"I can't help wondering what treasure would be found if only we could or knew how to test all those compounds in the right way. There are, for instance, many compounds which are not toxic but which were not tested in man because, on the basis of what are really crude animal tests, they did not seem to have especially promising biological effects. More of these ought to be studied in man.

"Actually, we don't even test all really interesting laboratory compounds because of the shortage of qualified clinical investigators. Who knows what cures for disease would be found if it were possible to increase the number of compounds given a thorough clinical trial!"

15 | *Pharmaceutical Engineering*

In a time of systematic medical and pharmaceutical research, new drugs and medicinal preparations will be derived from a very wide variety of sources. In the Upjohn Company, the largest number stem from work in the research division: from study of hormones and other basic biological studies, from chemical modification and "tailoring" of substances with interesting biological actions, from screening procedures. Some come from doctors in the medical division, who keep in touch with trends and needs in the medical profession. Lipomul i.v.—the unique high-calorie fat emulsion for intravenous feeding recently developed by Upjohn—came about through the medical department's interest in studies by Dr. Frederick J. Stare of Harvard on feeding very ill patients by vein. Dr. Stare's studies focused attention on the need for high-calorie nourishment that could be given by vein without causing reactions. It took Upjohn chemists eleven years to develop a suitable preparation.

Useful new products can also come from putting a drug into a new form for administration to the patient. A short time ago, Medrol, the Upjohn anti-inflammatory steroid, was prepared in the form of capsules made up of small pellets coated with a substance resistant to stomach acids but soluble in intestinal digestive juices. When one of the new Medule capsules (as they have been named) is swallowed, it breaks up into its constituent pellets, which then pass one at a time from the stomach to the small intestine, where the pellets are dissolved and their contents gradually absorbed into the blood stream. As a result, a longer, smoother action of the hormonal agent is obtained and the over-all dosage of Medrol required may even be reduced for some patients—a gain because patients should be given the least amount of a drug that will produce a desired medical effect.

The Medule development is interesting for two reasons. One is that the Upjohn Company started with Dr. W. E. Upjohn's invention of a new dosage form, the friable pill. The second is that, even today, the process of converting laboratory drugs into products capable of being administered to as many patients and as many different kinds of patients as may need them is by no means wholly routine.

In the past two or three decades, the discovery of new drugs has overshadowed the process of getting drugs out of the laboratory and onto drugstore shelves. Almost everyone knows that it took some doing to accomplish this for penicillin and cortisone. For most other drugs, the process is taken for granted.

It is true that many once difficult procedures in manufacturing drugs are now easily done. Few pharmaceutical firms have any trouble producing compressed tablets (which comprise 60 per cent of the solid oral medication taken by Americans) with a specified dose of medication. Gelatin capsules of all shapes, sizes, and types are turned out and filled by the tens of millions by high-speed automatic machines. Products which must be supplied in sterile form (sterile goods comprise nearly 10 per cent of Upjohn production) are treated and packed by methods that provide greater assurance of sterility than possible in the surgical operating room. A good deal of work is still required to develop a drug from the point where the research laboratory leaves off, however, as evidenced by the fact that the process may take several years.

Aside from passing successfully through animal and clinical tests to demonstrate safety and efficacy, a new drug must meet numerous requirements. A way must be found, first, to produce it in necessary quantities. Further, the drug must be put into a form that the patient can and will take and which will do what the prescribing doctor expects it to do. So far as possible, drugs must also be made proof against deterioration from age, light, heat, moisture, and other destructive conditions that may be encountered during the journey from manufacturing plant to patient. A change due to storage may alter the potency of a drug by less than 1 per cent, yet radically change its color or give it an off taste or odor; physicians will not be very willing to prescribe or patients to take it. Finally, this being a cantankerous world, a medicine to be taken by mouth, must have, if not a pleasant flavor, then one not so unpleasant that the patient will refuse to take it twice.

Pharmacists and pharmaceutical manufacturers have a term, "pharmaceutical elegance," having to do with clear sparkling solutions of pleasing color, and tablets and capsules of attractive appearance, free from chips or imperfections, and each tablet or capsule an exact counterpart of the next tablet or capsule in the bottle. In the eleventh century, Avicenna, the illustrious Arab physician, hit upon the device of coating pills with gold or silver foil to confer eye appeal upon them. Gold, silver, and aluminum foil (used for a time in the nineteenth century) have lost their standing as aids to pharmaceutical elegance. But medicines ought to possess it, for like a clean factory, pharmaceutical elegance bespeaks care in manufacturing. Patients and physicians have a right to expect and ought to find visible evidence of such care in the medicines they buy.

In the Kalamazoo pharmaceutical concern, the task of converting medicinal agents discovered in the research laboratory into practically useful mass-produced drugs falls chiefly to three development groups at Portage Road. One scales up the production of chemical substances. Another does the same for antibiotics. The third works out the compounding of basic medicinal chemicals and antibiotics into final dosage form. The three groups have some 150 scientific, engineering, and technical employees among them. They not only carry new Upjohn drugs through the pilot plant and into full-scale production as finished pharmaceuticals, but they prepare supplies of new drugs for clinical trial. (The quantities of new drugs consumed in clinical trials have become so large that they can no longer be prepared in the research laboratory.)

The activities of the chemical and antibiotic production groups often border closely upon basic research. For unless the research laboratory's method of preparing a new medicinal chemical is simple and economical, the chemical development group will seek a new process—an undertaking which more than once has proved as arduous as the research that led to the original discovery of the drug. In the case of new antibiotics, the antibiotic development unit assumes the entire task of learning how best to cultivate the antibiotic-producing microorganism and how to recover and purify the antibiotic. The microbiologists in the research laboratories downtown limit their work essentially to finding the new antibiotics.

The antibiotic development group has another, even more challenging responsibility: research on the basic antibiotic manufacturing process itself. Antibiotics are all produced to this day by batch processes. A fermenter is supplied with the proper nutrients, adjusted to suitable conditions of temperature, aeration, and so forth, and seeded with spores of the antibiotic-producing mold. Some days later, the fermenter is shut down, the brew pumped out, and the antibiotic recovered. The process is then begun over again. Like development research units in many other pharmaceutical plants throughout the world, Upjohn's antibiotic development unit has been seeking a continuous method of producing antibiotics—a method that would allow antibiotics to be drawn off continuously from the fermenting mash without stopping the whole process and while the mold continued to grow and produce. Such a scheme would greatly reduce the cost of producing antibiotics, especially some of the newer, more expensive ones. But so far, none of the antibiotic molds has been at all cooperative. Most will continue to grow in the fermenter, as long as nutrients are added and proper conditions are maintained, but the yield of antibiotics falls sharply after a few days. So the fermenters must still be shut down and restarted with fresh mold spores every few days.

As a matter of fact few antibiotic molds have yet approached the productiveness of either the penicillin or streptomycin mold. During the past two decades, the yield of penicillin per gallon of mash has been boosted by improved nutrients, better methods of cultivation, the development of more active strains of mold, and innumerable other stratagems to a level thousands of times greater than the yields obtained by Fleming, Florey, and Chain. Streptomycin yields have been raised to a comparable degree. But few other antibiotic molds have been persuaded to do better than half as well. The Albamycin mold in particular has been a balky performer. The yield has been raised substantially above the levels obtained when it was first discovered and put into production. Despite continuous efforts by the antibiotic development unit to improve matters, however, the yield remained (at least through 1959) below that of the tetracyclines, making Albamycin an expensive antibiotic to produce.

The compounding of medicines is an old art. Even such characteristic occupants of the modern medicine chest as the gelatin capsule and compressed tablet have a long history. The gelatin capsule was invented by a Monsieur de Mothe in France in 1833. The compressed tablet also goes well back, although it did not come into wide use until the 1890s; an English pharmacist named Brockedon made the first compressed tablet in 1843. The National Formulary and other standard volumes for the pharmaceutical art have long listed numerous binders, diluents, and coating agents for tablets and flavors and taste-masking agents for fluid medicines.

As a result, there is no end of experience and practical knowledge available when the Upjohn pharmaceutical development group sets about turning a new drug, sent to it from the research laboratory via the chemical or the antibiotic development unit, into a finished pharmaceutical. But new times and new products create new problems and demand new advances in the compounding art. Over 90 per cent of the prescriptions now written in the United States are for drugs put into final form in the pharmaceutical plant rather than by the local druggist (who could not, for technical reasons, compound a majority of them even if he wished).

A few drugs can be pressed directly into tablets possessing the desired combination of keeping qualities, freedom from chipping and breakage, and just-right firmness. ("A good finished uncoated tablet," says *Remington's Practice of Pharmacy,* the bible of pharmacy, "will be firm enough to just break between the second and third fingers when using the thumb fingernail as a fulcrum." Or to crush to a powder under the thumb, as with the friable pills of Dr. Upjohn.) Most drugs, however, require treatment with one or more binders, diluents, absorbents, moisteners, stabilizers, lubricants, or coating materials to form them into acceptable tablets. Sucrose, ordinary sugar, is a frequently used coating material and illustrates well the properties a coating material must have; it has a pleasant taste, is a good binder, interferes with few medicinal agents, takes color well, can be polished to an attractive sheen, dissolves quickly in the stomach, and is easily applied. For enteric coatings (applied to tablets designed to dissolve in the small intestine rather than the stomach), there are several new materials to supplement the pharmacist's old standby, the highly refined grade of shellac known as "pharmacist's shellac."

Lately, tablets have become increasingly complex and sophisticated. One major innovation is the prolonged-release tablet, as employed in Medules and utilized today in one form or another for an ever-growing list of medications. Another modern development is the compound tablet combining into a single dose two or more substances that may be companionable in the body (and are all needed for the patient's treatment), yet are incompatible in the pill. In some preparations, the problem of incompatibility can be solved by putting the troublesome ingredients in more stable form. In others, it has been ingeniously dealt with by constructing a tablet with a separate core or separate layers or by providing in some other way separate housing for the incompatible substances.

A task which still causes the pharmaceutical chemist considerable difficulty is the preparation of satisfactory fluid medicines, especially suspensions. Prominent among fluid medicines are antibiotic preparations intended for children, who—however capable some youngsters seem at swallowing inexplicably large numbers of aspirin tablets—often cannot take or be persuaded to take solid medication. Unfortunately, several of the most useful antibiotics do not dissolve well in water or other acceptable solvents and, when put up as fluids, must be prepared in the form of suspensions. It would be useful to have a method of stabilizing suspensions, so that the medication would not settle out for a period of several years at least, and thus provide the patient with the intended dose of medicine whether anyone remembers to "shake well before using" or not. Research is bringing progress toward that goal, but for many important fluid medicines, it has not yet been reached. In the meantime, preparations like Panalba, the tetracycline-Albamycin combination, must be put out for pediatric use as flavored granules, to be mixed with water and made into a suspension when used.

In spite of the number of flavoring agents available, taste can also still be a problem in fluid medicines. Aside from the fact that some obvious choices, such as chocolate, are seldom used because of the possibility of allergy, new drugs introduce new taste interactions between medication and flavoring agent. To guide the choice of flavoring agent, pharmaceutical firms often employ panels of tasters to sample new fluid medicines. Upjohn's tasters are twenty-five employees selected from several hundred for their ability to discriminate between closely similar flavors and to identify the same flavor reliably in repeated tests. Curiously, most of the successful candidates for the taste panel have been young women. Oddly enough, though, the most popular flavor in Upjohn history—the tart cherry flavor of Cheracol—was selected for the cough medicine 3½ decades ago by Dr. Heyl, the company research director, without benefit of taste panel. But the panel has been successful in consistently choosing for Upjohn's pediatric medicine flavors that allow the medicines to be swallowed without protest by the immense majority of junior patients.

There are times when it must seem that the pharmaceutical

development group is doing its work almost too well. A few years ago, several investigators called attention to the fact that many nonsterile eye ointments were on the market and that even sterile ointments could become a source of contamination as a result of the widespread practice of using a single tube of ointment for more than one application to the eye. The Upjohn Company decided to develop a product to avoid this possible hazard. At considerable cost and with some difficulty—ointments are not easy to sterilize, as most are destroyed by heat and it is difficult to make sure that chemical germicides reach all parts of the ointment—a sterile ointment in a single-dose tube was prepared. It was, of course, more expensive than conventional ointments, and it had to be opened with a sterile scissors. Though much had been said of the need for such a preparation, almost no one bought it and it had to be withdrawn. (Incidentally, further experience has shown eye ointments not to be a frequent source of eye infections.)

The diverse activities of the three development groups—chemical, antibiotic, and pharmaceutical—not only play an essential part in bringing medicines from the laboratory to the patient. Together with their opposite numbers in other pharmaceutical firms, they have built up a distinctive technology which, oddly enough, has yet to acquire a name. The new technology borrows elements from chemistry, microbiology, pharmacology, pharmacy, and other scientific and technical disciplines, along with techniques from the research man and the engineer, all for the purpose of mass-producing potent new medicines in ready-to-use form. What the pharmaceutical industry's development people are doing constitutes a new field, pharmaceutical engineering.

16 | Even Medicines Must Be Sold

Pharmaceutical firms, especially large ones like the Upjohn Company, have sometimes been described, with tongue in cheek perhaps, as arrangements for generating a steady flow of new products from the research laboratory to the sales department. The remark points up an uncomfortable conflict between the ideal and the real in the practice of medicine. In the ideal world, the physician needs no prompting to keep up with significant new developments in medicine. His patients always receive the benefit of the most effective treatment.

Reality inevitably departs from the ideal in numerous particulars. Medicine is becoming ever more complex, medical progress swifter. There are no longer hours enough in the

225

day—even if he did nothing else—for a physician to keep fully informed of important advances in the various branches of medicine. A substantial majority of young physicians become specialists for this reason as well as for the economic advantages of specialty practice.

In the past few decades, medical schools and the medical profession have erected an impressive apparatus for refreshing the physician's knowledge and keeping it up to date. In a recent year, medical schools, teaching hospitals, and organizations like the American College of Physicians offered more than 2,000 one- to two-week postgraduate courses, covering almost every conceivable medical subject, for practicing physicians. Major hospitals regularly demonstrate methods of diagnosis and treatment on teaching rounds of their wards. Medical societies conduct lectures and forums. Medical publishers issue a vast number of books and journals; at last count there were some 700 journals in the medical and allied fields in the United States alone.

Unhappily, these efforts neither reach all doctors nor are they uniformly effective. A few years ago, nearly 5,000 physicians were questioned in a study sponsored by the American Medical Association as to what they did to keep up. The study showed that many put in over 500 hours—equivalent to more than 60 eight-hour days—a year attending lectures and refresher courses and taking part in other activities designed to keep them informed. But 30 per cent said that they practiced too far from medical education centers, or were too busy, or, for some other reason, were unable to take part in organized postgraduate educational activities. Many more who reported making a systematic effort to keep up felt that some activities like lectures were often of limited value and said that it was impossible to take postgraduate courses more than once every few years. It takes a special effort to bring new information—even of significant advances—to the entire medical profession quickly.

The pharmaceutical industry carries on a very large volume and very large variety of activities designed to call the attention of doctors to new drugs. Some of these activities are disinterestedly educational; most are related to specific products. The great volume of such activity—and the unfortunate shrillness of a portion of it—are a direct result of the large number of competing pharmaceutical firms. In any event, pharmaceutical promotion has had a direct part in the rapid introduction of important new drugs from the time of the sulfonamides and penicillin forward.

The most effective means of introducing new drugs is the pharmaceutical company "detail man" who calls on physicians. The AMA survey of how doctors keep up quoted two thirds of the physicians questioned as saying that the greatest part of their information on new drugs comes from detail men. In fact, the well-trained detail man—who is more of a technical representative than a salesman—can furnish information on a new drug of a kind the doctor cannot easily obtain elsewhere. The detail man not only carries with him samples of the drug and reprints of medical journal articles evaluating it and describing its use; he also has systematic data on the drug's basic properties. Such data is seldom printed in full in the general medical journals most physicians see.

As the Upjohn Company has grown over the years, its sales, promotion, and educational activities have expanded in

range as well as scale. Sometimes as often as several times a
year, it has presented a well-received closed-circuit television
program for doctors called "Grand Rounds" in which distinguished specialists from all parts of the United States and
abroad have been brought before the television camera to
demonstrate and discuss up-to-the-minute diagnostic and
treatment techniques. Another venture is a sprightly newspaper, *Scope Weekly,* to provide physicians with fast, accurate
news of medical developments, before (as many doctors com-
plain in this day of widespread science and medical news
reporting) "patients read about them in the newspapers and
tell us." Other activities include the preparation of medical
teaching films and of exhibits for medical meetings. A spectacular recent creation was a whopping walk-in model of a
living cell, as delineated by the latest findings of biological
research; the model was 24 feet in diameter and 12 feet high.
(After exhibit at several medical meetings, the huge model
was a feature display at the Chicago Museum of Science and
Industry, then crossed the Atlantic to serve in a British Broad-
casting Corporation cellular biology television program.) An
electronic model of the brain, 20 feet in diameter and 11 feet
high and illustrating how the brain functions (rather than
how it looks), is another recent special Upjohn medical exhibit. In addition, the Kalamazoo firm is an active advertiser
in medical journals and through direct mail to physicians and
druggists, and it prepares counter displays for major non-
prescription vitamin products.

The main focus of the Upjohn sales and promotion effort,
however, is its staff of more than 1,000 detail men. The Upjohn detail force is one of the largest in the pharmaceutical
industry. Competitors also say it is "just about tops." "Up-

john is one of the most conservative houses in the industry in promotion," declares the sales manager of another large pharmaceutical firm. "But it can get 10 per cent of the market on any drug it chooses to sell, even if half a dozen other firms have the drug out first." ("Nice to hear how well we can sell," comments an Upjohn sales executive. "Wish it were true.")

Both Upjohn's detailing force and the institution of detailing in general are worth examining for a moment. Upjohn detail men are officially titled "sales representatives," and most have the functions of both the salesman and the technical representative, for they call on both druggists and doctors. Most Upjohn products, however, are sold chiefly through drugstores. Druggists are therefore the individuals who actually place the orders for most Upjohn products, including the drugs for which the doctor writes the prescription.

Almost all the Kalamazoo company's detail men are college graduates with their primary training in pharmacy, chemistry, or biology. At one time, the majority were pharmacists. However, the expansion of the pharmaceutical industry and of the retail drug business has made pharmacists hard to get. Today, many are premedical students who decide not to go through with medical school. (In recent years, early marriage has steered many able premedical students away from medical school and into other jobs. Premedical students unable to make the grade scholastically, on the other hand, are not sought.) Physical education majors have also been found to make effective detail men; physical education majors nowadays receive a good grounding in biology in many schools.

Upjohn detail men are paid a straight salary. This allows

the company to decide what products it wants detailed and avoids the problem of high-pressure selling of a few of the most popular products in order to boost commissions. An extensive, nearly continuous training program not only provides technical information on Upjohn products but teaches the detail man how to detail.

The detail men work out of Upjohn's branch offices, through which Upjohn's products are distributed and of which there are now eighteen throughout the United States. Each man has a specific territory, usually containing the offices of up to a few hundred doctors (depending on the territory), a smaller number of dentists, and several drugstores. Several small hospitals may be included in a territory. In the largest cities, hospitals are handled by a separate hospital detailing staff. Veterinary products are detailed by still another separate group.

Detail men's visits to doctors are brief, lasting as a rule no more than fifteen minutes or so. When the Upjohn representative comes in with the brown alligator sample-and-literature bag—which Upjohn adopted fifty years ago as an identifying mark for its representatives—he must be prepared to discuss briefly one or more Upjohn products of potential interest to the doctor.

"A good detail man never advises a doctor to use a particular product," says an Upjohn branch manager. "That would be telling a doctor how to practice medicine—and a good way to be shown the door fast. Whether the physician prescribes the product for his patients, and how long, is up to him and his own experience with it.

"The detail man's job is to summarize the properties and characteristics of the drug, the experience of investigators and other physicians in using it as reported in medical journals, and indications and contraindications as to use. He also answers any questions the physician may have or arranges to get answers from the company's medical division. And, of course, he usually leaves samples and medical journal reprints and other literature."

A "canned" recital is not used. ("That would cause real trouble—there are plenty of doctors who don't mind throwing monkey wrenches in canned spiels.") And candor is the rule with the experienced detailer with regard to contraindications (situations in which the drug should not be used) and possible toxicity.

The average detail man calls on an average of four or five physicians a day. Interestingly, even in citadels of big-city cynicism and the olympian aloofness of university medical schools, Upjohn men have long enjoyed a good entree. On reflection, though, this should hardly be surprising. Metropolitan and medical-school physicians are well-known for their interest in practicing the best and most modern type of medicine and in new medicinal preparations that can assist their patients—just the sort of product that has been emerging ever more frequently in recent years from the pharmaceutical laboratory. Whether or not he will wish to use any given new drug, the alert doctor is anxious to learn as much as he can about as many new drugs as he can.

The successful marketing of a new drug and the size of market it may attain are a compound of many factors. The drug must first of all be useful and, preferably, unique, that is, provide effective treatment for an ailment for which only ineffective or much less effective treatment existed before. It must also have to do with a widespread ailment if it is to attain a large market; a specific for an uncommon fungus infection cannot be expected to have as large a sale as a specific for arthritis. Further, the safer and simpler to use the better. In this cantankerous world, people shy away from difficulties; and if it is possible to make a mistake in using a drug, someone will make it. And the new drug must be properly launched.

The last stricture can apply even to a highly unusual, much-wanted drug. When Orinase was launched in 1957, a good many Upjohn men felt that the Kalamazoo firm at last had a product that would require little "selling." The long, extensive clinical trial and the enormous newspaper and magazine publicity Orinase received as the first safe oral drug for diabetes made it seem as though the Upjohn sales department would be, for once, merely order takers. It was not so. Because of the inherent risks in the treatment of diabetes with insulin, many physicians had long since made it a practice to refer diabetic patients to colleagues specializing in the disease. Many were fearful that Orinase might involve similar risks, and they were persuaded of the drug's safety only by the great mass of scientific literature attesting to its safety and usefulness and called to their attention by the detail men.

A new drug must be prepared for market as well as discovered, tested, and manufactured. A key part of the marketing process is the selection of a suitable name. Chemical nomenclature having become unpronounceably clumsy and people (including doctors) having an undeniable preference for easy-to-remember names, a search is made for a simple and euphonious yet distinctive name. Words utilizing a syllable or two of the drug's chemical name or with a clear association with the properties of the drug are preferred (e.g., Provera, the new *pro*gesterone derivative, and Albamycin, a name derived from the white color of the mold culture); names implying medical usefulness (for example, "Cold Tablets" or "Pneumonia Remedy") are taboo under the Food, Drug, and Cosmetic Act. In any event, simple appropriate names are becoming difficult to find. In Upjohn, the responsibility for choosing names rests on a trademark committee headed by the company's chief attorney. But others are welcome to contribute. The lawyers will have the last word anyway, for every plausible candidate must be checked with trademark lists to make sure the candidate does not infringe on someone else's trade name.

A decision must also be made as to whether and how the drug is to be marketed. Not all drugs that could be marketed are actually placed on sale; a drug has to show a distinct margin of superiority over existing agents or have some other compelling circumstance in its favor to be put on the list. Moreover, some drugs must be marketed without the benefit of intensive detailing, for not all drugs can be detailed. When a detail man calls on a physician, his "detail" will usually include no more than four products. Of these, he may discuss no more than two or three, or only one, either because of lack of time or because not all doctors are interested in all products. (A skin specialist, for example, has little interest in a drug for heart disease.) Since the detail man can visit each physician only several times a year, no more than twenty to thirty drugs can be detailed per year—and some of the places on the list must be reserved for older products of importance or repeat detailing of major new products. Orinase was detailed for nearly a year.

The main burden of deciding what to do and how to do it rests chiefly on a group under W. Fred Allen, the sales department veteran who is currently vice-president for marketing. A decision to put a new product on sale, even one which is not likely to have a wide enough market to be put on the list for detailing, sets the machine in motion. Company branches and retail druggists must be stocked. (At their own request, a large majority of the 55,000 drugstores in the United States are automatically stocked in advance of sale with all new Upjohn products.) Instructional and promotional literature must be prepared and other promotional activities set in train.

Much depends on making the right decision, at this point as all along the line. A product unwisely marketed can be costly. A product prematurely scrapped or inadequately promoted—there have been many useful pharmaceutical products that died because they were poorly sold—can be costly in other ways. A product that seems just what the doctor ordered can be made obsolete before it has reached the drugstore by a superior competing product.

The record makes it clear, however, that the pill company started by the inventive doctor from Kalamazoo has more than survived these and other vicissitudes. Few business institutions can match its record for sustained growth or its successful turn into an area of new discovery and rapid advance whose full dimensions the Upjohn Company's founder could hardly have foreseen.

17 | *Medicine Makers of Kalamazoo*

Until the late fall of 1958, the name of the Upjohn Company was familiar to few people outside the medical profession, the retail drug trade and the pharmaceutical industry. One reason for this was Upjohn's policy, as an ethical manufacturer of pharmaceuticals, of advertising and promoting its medicinal products to the medical profession only. Another was the fact that the company was essentially a family enterprise, with a comparatively small number of stockholders. Its stock was not listed on any exchange and it did not publish its financial reports.

Going back to the time in 1909 when Dr. W. E. Upjohn had bought out his brothers and acquired virtually all the company's stock, the largest share of Upjohn stock was held by Dr. W. E.'s direct descendants—the families of his son W. Harold Upjohn and of his three daughters (one of whom is married to board chairman and managing director Gilmore; another had been the wife of Dr. S. Rudolph Light, the company's director of production until 1930). Smaller blocks of stock were owned by other relatives, a number of key employees and their heirs, and philanthropic and community institutions. Although Upjohn was not a close corporation in the legal sense (i.e., only employees and close relatives of employees permitted to own stock), little stock was held by anyone without a direct connection with either company or family.

Aside from the fact that the company's history made such a pattern of ownership inevitable, it had several real advantages for the Kalamazoo concern. One, of course, was to assure continuation of the Upjohn Company as a family undertaking. In addition, closely held companies can arrive at decisions quickly. Policies that are often difficult for publicly held corporations to agree to are readily carried out. During its long history, for example, the Upjohn Company had consistently followed a conservative dividend policy. It did not have to heed the clamor of stockholders to pay out the greater part of earnings as dividends, as publicly held corporations must sometimes do, but was able to retain them for reinvestment in the company. As a result, right back to its earliest years, Upjohn's steady growth has been financed largely out of earnings. Even the great Portage Road plant and general office project was financed substantially without outside borrowing. Likewise, Upjohn's pioneering in such areas as shorter hours, weekly salaries for production workers, and group life insurance and other employee benefits was facilitated by the company's limited number of stockholders. But times change, and so do laws—especially tax laws. As witness the changes in the Ford Motor Company after the death of Henry Ford in 1947, family-held business firms have found the going heavy in the contemporary United States.

In the case of Upjohn, recent years began to bring increasingly serious disadvantages—both for the company and its stockholders—in close, essentially family ownership. One of the most conspicuous was the lack of a stable, realistic price for Upjohn stock.

In 1955, the United States Treasury set a value of $282.50 a share on Upjohn stock for gift- and inheritance-tax purposes. A handful of shares, however, had been sold on the over-the-counter market through stockbrokers by individuals who had inherited the stock or had formerly worked for Upjohn. These shares were occasionally traded and brought whopping prices—sometimes over three times the Treasury valuation—in part because of the bright future of the pharmaceutical industry generally and Upjohn in particular and, to some small extent, because executives of competing pharmaceutical firms sought to buy Upjohn stock both as an investment and to gain access to Upjohn financial reports. At one point, in 1958, Upjohn stock was selling for as high as $2,050 a share over the counter.

The lack of a realistic value for the stock made it difficult for the Kalamazoo company to utilize one of the most effective means by which corporations finance improvement and the establishment or acquisition of useful new subsidiaries— the issuance of new stock. Even more important from the point of view of day-to-day operation, Upjohn found it extremely difficult to work out a rational stock option plan for executives. In the present era of high personal income taxes, business firms have found it all but impossible to attract able executives without offering them an opportunity to buy company stock on favorable terms (and thus build an estate) as a supplement to their salaries. But the first step toward setting up a sound stock option plan is a realistic valuation of the stock.

The absence of a genuine market and market price for Upjohn stock also created numerous problems—some decidedly bizarre—for stockholders. It was even difficult to give the pharmaceutical company's stock away. Some members of the family were anxious to donate stock to provide funds for the construction of a new Kalamazoo art center. Tax laws require the placing of a money value upon philanthropic gifts. And the center would have to be free to sell the stock for construction cash.

More urgent was the fact that several large stockholders were at or approaching an age when consideration of inheritance tax problems could not be escaped. When and as stockholders' estates came up for probate, the United States government was certain to place a new, higher valuation upon Upjohn stock. The sizable estate taxes this would lead to would inevitably force the sale of a substantial part of the stockholders' holdings. But who would buy the stock? Certainly not stockholders who were already faced with inheritance tax difficulties because of their Upjohn holdings.

As early as 1955, some members of the family began considering converting the company to a publicly held corporation and selling a part of their holdings to the public. From time to time, informal discussions of the numerous problems going "public" would involve were held with a New York investment firm.

A public offering of Upjohn stock became more pressing as the result of a development early in 1958. A fairly substantial stockholder had placed a part of his stock on the open market. His name was Richard Sellman and he was assistant director of sales in charge of Upjohn's Western branches. Sellman had inherited a block of Upjohn stock from his father, Waters H. Sellman, who had represented Upjohn in San Francisco since before the San Francisco fire. Sellman determined to take advantage of the rise in drug stock prices in 1957–1958 to diversify his stockholdings and place himself in a better position for estate-tax purposes by selling part of his Upjohn stock. He arranged with Blyth & Company, a San Francisco brokerage house, to sell 1,327 shares for the best possible price up to $1,250 a share. Sellman's stipulated price was readily obtained.

In earlier times, Sellman's action would almost certainly have produced a demand for his resignation. In the 1930s and 1940s, it would still have aroused criticism in Kalamazoo. In 1958, when Sellman wrote the secretary of the company to inform him of his action, there were neither remonstrances nor serious regrets. Instead, major stockholders recognized that the time had come for them to make a similar move.

During the fall, the company's corporate registration was shifted from Michigan to Delaware, a state that issues less restrictive corporate charters. In addition, the stock was split 25 for 1 to bring the price down to the pocketbook of the average investor; altogether, 14,056,000 $1 par value shares in the new Delaware corporation were exchanged for approximately 560,000 $10 par value shares in the old Michigan company.

On December 11, major stockholders joined in offering some 17 per cent of their holdings through an underwriting syndicate organized by Morgan Stanley & Company of New York. Altogether, 2,410,000 of the new shares, worth $108 million, were put up for sale. It was the first formal stock offering in the company's history and the second largest secondary stock offering (i.e., stock issued without increasing a company's capital and not intended to raise "new money") on record. Only the first offering of Ford Motor stock by the Ford Foundation a few years ago exceeded the Upjohn offering among secondary stock offerings.

The excitement in Wall Street during the days before the sale nearly matched that preceding the big sale of Ford stock. The Upjohn offering was heavily oversubscribed. Within a few hours of the opening of the formal sale, Upjohn stockholders had grown in number from 500 to more than 29,000. Three and a half weeks later, Upjohn stock was listed on the big board, the New York Stock Exchange. A new corporate personality had appeared on the national financial scene.

When members of the public bought into the Kalamazoo pharmaceutical firm, what did they buy? To begin with, they bought into a firm which still has many of the characteristics of a family undertaking. Upjohns continue to be major stockholders and to work for the company in a wide variety of posts. Secondly, the public bought into one of the largest pharmaceutical houses in the United States. In 1959—the last year for which figures are available—Upjohn had sales of $157 million.

More than 5,500 people work for Upjohn, 3,500 of them in Kalamazoo, which has become a diversified manufacturing town in the seventy-five years since the company was founded and which has a current population of 80,000. Only one Kalamazoo firm, a paper company, is a larger employer. Upjohn headquarters is in a new general office building, a two-level 350-foot-square structure built around a series of open areas, enclosed courts, and covered terraces. Located on Portage Road south of Kalamazoo, it is the Michigan city's most modern structure (the Frank Lloyd Wright homes built by a group of local residents not excepted). A group of new buildings across Portage Road from the office building houses all manufacturing activities and gives Upjohn the only pharmaceutical plant in the United States entirely built since World War II. The main manufacturing building, a low, nearly square yellow brick structure, is almost a mile around. The six blocks of buildings downtown—once the main manufacturing plant—are now given over almost entirely to research and related activities. In addition, Upjohn operates a 1,600-acre farm at Richland, a village northeast of Kalamazoo, and a lodge and guest houses near Augusta, to the east. The farm is used for veterinary and agricultural research. The lodge and guest houses—known as Brook Lodge and built around Dr. W. E. Upjohn's former summer home—are utilized for scientific, sales, and other company conferences and for visitors on company business.

As is the case in most modern industrial firms, fewer than 1 Upjohn employee in 4 is directly engaged in production. The others are employed in the host of other tasks required to keep a modern pharmaceutical organization in business.

Some 125 are employed upon just the one task—especially crucial in a pharmaceutical firm—of control, checking on the purity of both raw materials and finished products, guaranteeing that 5-grain tablets actually contain 5 grains of medication, testing sterile goods for bacterial contamination, and so forth. Over 700 (well over one-third of whom have doctoral degrees in science or medicine) are engaged in research—the great majority in the search for, and the evaluation of, new drugs and in other laboratory research, but many in the tasks of developing production methods and putting Upjohn products into final medicinal form. Many hundreds of other employees are engaged in maintenance, shipping, accounting, prosecution of patent claims, preparation of package inserts (instructional material inserted in drug packages, required by Federal law for most drugs), recruitment of new personnel, and the myriad other tasks essential to a pharmaceutical enterprise. Several hundred work in the network of Upjohn branches. More than 1,000 employees are salesmen calling on hospitals, drugstores, and physicians.

Most pharmaceutical products, whether taken by mouth, given by injection, or, say, sprayed into the nose, wind up inside the body. As a result, pharmaceutical firms make special efforts to keep their plants clean. At Upjohn, housekeeping is made a responsibility of the entire production force; each production crew in the vast Portage Road plant is expected to keep its area in order. The system works. Visitors (who are welcome to all parts of the main plant, except the sterile-goods units and a few other areas where visitors might interfere with the work) seldom fail to remark that the floor looks clean enough to eat from.

Upjohn's system of putting plant housekeeping up to individual production crews is a natural outgrowth of a twofold company policy of providing as pleasant a place to work as possible and leaving as much as possible to the individual employee. Thus, there are no time clocks. All employees are on weekly salary and simply fill out cards (without which it would be impossible to compute overtime payments) showing the number of hours worked. No wages are docked for absence due to illness, nor is a doctor's certificate required. Supervisors are authorized to accept any reasonable excuse for absence or lateness. Similarly, employees are expected to take a morning and afternoon coffee break in low-priced snack bars operated by the company. Lunch-hour recreational facilities at Portage Road are so numerous and the atmosphere so relaxed that the plant has been described as a country club with working privileges.

H. E. Turbeville, vice-president and director of personnel for more than two decades, explains that Upjohn is confident of its employees' honesty and feels that most want to do a good job. No point is seen therefore to rules that penalize the great majority merely in order to control an irresponsible few. Upjohn, at any rate, has no problem with lateness and its absence rate is well below the average for United States industry. Production per employee, moreover, has risen steadily through the years.

All Upjohn employees, including production workers, are on salary; there are no hourly-rated employees in the company. The work week is the standard forty hours except during the summer when employees go on a thirty-five hour week—at forty hours' pay. Though wages are computed on a weekly basis, hourly rates of pay average out to about the rates for comparable work in the Kalamazoo area and in the pharmaceutical industry generally. However, Upjohn employees receive unusually large additional benefits. Among them are a long-established paid vacation plan; life insurance entirely paid for by the company up to $2,000 per employee, with additional insurance available (subject to certain limitations) on a contributory basis; and company-paid accidental death and dismemberment insurance. Medical- and surgical-expense insurance are also provided at company expense, and the company pays the greatest part of the cost of employee hospital insurance. Other benefits include a retirement plan which (together with Social Security) pays pensions of up to 65 per cent of the employee's earnings in the best five of his or her last ten years with the company; preretirement death benefits are also paid. The retirement plan was originally a contributory scheme; in 1955, the company assumed all costs of the plan and returned contributions previously paid by employees. In addition, Upjohn makes the required contributions to Social Security and the state unemployment insurance plan.

Even more important in making the Kalamazoo pharmaceutical firm an attractive place of employment is a practice of making most promotions from within the company and the fact that there has never been a shutdown because of lack of work. In part the latter is due to Upjohn's extraordinary record of steady growth (maintained even during the Great Depression). But in part it is owing also to the absence of rigid job classifications among its production workers. (There is no union at Upjohn and hence no spelling out and freezing of job classifications as occurs in many union contracts. Although other industries in Kalamazoo and pharmaceutical plants elsewhere are unionized, attempts to organize Upjohn have evoked little response.) As a consequence, production employees are easily shifted to other work when a particular production line is shut down, whether because of seasonal changes in the demand for different products or because a given product has been superseded by something better.

Whatever else they may accomplish, Upjohn's personnel policies have received a decisive stamp of approval from at least one segment of its fellow citizens of Kalamazoo. The company has an average of eight applicants for every job opening.

The Upjohn Company's liberal policy toward employees is no doubt motivated in good part by a belief that it is good for the company. The policy may also reflect the sentiment of an old local family for neighbors. Unlike many that acquire wealth from a business enterprise, the Upjohn family has not moved away and become an absentee owner. After a century and a quarter, it remains very much a part of the Kalamazoo scene. Many Upjohns and Upjohn in-laws still live in Kalamazoo—indeed, chiefly within the town itself rather than in the suburbs that have sprung up in recent decades. And Kalamazoo is dotted with community institutions aided or launched by members of the family.

There is, for instance, the Kalamazoo Foundation, launched in 1925 by Dr. W. E. Upjohn with a modest cash gift and a sizable bequest of Upjohn stock after Dr. W. E.'s death. By 1959, the Kalamazoo Foundation, which administers gifts as well as makes grants out of its own funds and which had grown into the third largest community foundation in the United States, had distributed over $3 million to seventy-two local agencies and institutions. Thanks in large part to Up-johns, Kalamazoo has a Civic Auditorium, complete with symphony orchestra, little theater group, and other activities. Dr. W. E. (whose numerous philanthropies and civic enter-prises have already been related in more detail) provided the auditorium and initial operating funds; two daughters and a son-in-law (Mrs. Dorothy Dalton and Mr. and Mrs. Donald Gilmore) contributed to the construction of Carver Center, the auditorium's auxiliary building. Kalamazoo Col-lege—a liberal arts college and one of Kalamazoo's two main institutions of higher learning, the other being Western Michigan University—has been aided by several Upjohns, including the Light branch of the family, connected with Dr. W. E. Upjohn through daughter Winifred Upjohn Light; Dr. Richard Upjohn Light served as chairman of the college board of trustees during a critical period of growth. A gift by Grace Upjohn, widow of Harold Upjohn, Dr. W. E.'s only son, made possible the Harold Upjohn School for Handi-capped Children. Recently, the Gilmores—Donald and Jane —provided funds for an art center building.

The principal evidence of the family in Kalamazoo, how-ever, remains the company bearing its name. A few months after Upjohn became a public company, the company pub-lished its first annual report. The report, together with other recent company publications, painted a revealing picture of the Kalamazoo firm.

Few United States companies can match Upjohn's record of steady growth. The year 1959 marked the thirty-eighth successive year of growth in sales—usually by about 10 per cent a year. Profits had also increased through the years, but not so steadily. Dips in earnings (though no losses) had occurred during and after World War I, in 1926, early in World War II (in part because of wartime taxes), and again when antibiotic prices broke in 1950–1952. Profits have been near the pharmaceutical industry average.

The reports also reveal the origin of Upjohn's uninterrupted growth. In the past two years, the leading Upjohn products, in terms of sales, have been Albamycin, Medrol, and Orinase. None existed five years ago. Over 90 per cent of the Kalamazoo company's current sales are of products unknown a generation ago. By far the greater part of the company's output, in short, stems from research—in good measure, its own research.

In years past, the larger pharmaceutical houses sometimes sought to be "full-line" houses, that is, marketers of everything the doctor might need in his practice. No pharmaceutical manufacturer could actually have achieved that goal in full, for no manufacturer's line took in the entire medical armamentarium, though some firms came close. Today, no firm can be really strongly represented in all forms of medication, for medicinal products have become too diversified and research and development costs too high to make this feasible. The Upjohn Company is nevertheless well represented in most of the major areas of modern pharmaceuticals. It is a leading producer of vitamins as well as hormones, of the outstanding oral antidiabetic as well as widely used antibiotics. It produces staples, such as cough medicines, as well as specialties, such as anticoagulant drugs and Gelfoam, the absorbable sponge.

Recently, moreover, the Kalamazoo company has begun to broaden out in other ways. It is manufacturing hormones, hormone intermediates, and other fine chemicals not only for its own use, but for sale in bulk to other pharmaceutical firms. And Upjohn products have finally begun to find their way in quantity to the corners of the world. Because of the high reputation of American pharmaceuticals abroad since World War II, the Upjohn Company decided in 1952 to reverse a historic policy and make a systematic effort to market Upjohn products overseas. By 1960, the Kalamazoo firm had wholly or jointly owned distributing subsidiaries operating in Canada, Great Britain, Australia, South Africa, France, Japan, Mexico, the Canal Zone, Colombia, and Brazil. Manufacturing plants were in operation in Canada (the only country outside the United States where Upjohn had had substantial sales before the decision to push into foreign markets), Mexico, and Australia. Upjohn pharmaceuticals were being produced under contract in Japan. Some two hundred of the Kalamazoo firm's products were being marketed abroad, and foreign sales represented over 10 per cent of the company's total output and were still going up.

18 | The Useful Cycle

The development of the Upjohn Company—like that of the pharmaceutical industry as a whole—can be looked at from a number of points of view. In surveying the Kalamazoo firm's first three-quarters of a century, we have sampled several. Something has been said of its origin and continuance as a family enterprise, of its growth as a business corporation, of specific accomplishments in medical and pharmaceutical research. Many business firms, however, originate as family undertakings. There are also many that prosper and grow and make scientific and technical advances. What sets the Upjohn Company apart is—along with other comparable pharmaceutical firms—its emergence as an effective device for accomplishing a distinctive, increasingly complex, socially

249

necessary object—the systematic discovery, development, and distribution of an expanding armamentarium of effective medicines.

When the means by which a society meets its needs and orders its affairs are examined, those that work best are usually found to be the ones that most successfully harness compelling social motives. The contemporary American pharmaceutical industry is an example. As pointed out a few years ago by Dr. Harry F. Dowling, head of the University of Illinois department of medicine, organizations like the Upjohn Company blend a diversity of forces. One is the patient's desire to get well and, coupled with that, the doctor's desire to get him well as quickly as possible. Another is the professional scientist's interest in research. Fourth is the desire of the stockholders and management of the company for profits. The willingness of the doctor to prescribe and the patient to pay for new medicines that work better than old provides profits to the manufacturer. The manufacturer invests part of his profits in further research to discover and develop new medicines in order to obtain new profits, and the cycle starts over again.

The working out of the cycle can be charted for both the pharmaceutical industry as a whole and Upjohn as an individual concern. In several firms, the money that financed the development of the sulfa drugs in the late 1930s came from profits on vitamins and vitamin products developed a few years before. Profits on sulfonamides furnished a sizable part of the research and development funds for antibiotics. Antibiotic profits in turn provided the money for the big breakthrough in cortisone and related hormones in a majority of the firms active in the cortical hormone field.

The Upjohn Company began with a profitable specialty, the friable pill and did not advance again until it had two others, Phenolax and Citrocarbonate. The latter financed the development of Upjohn's standardized digitalis preparation and Super D cod liver oil and other vitamin preparations. Vitamin products, especially Unicaps, paid for a long list of research developments before and after World War II, including heparin, Gelfoam, the bottle-process plant built by Upjohn as an emergency wartime source of penicillin, and hormones and hormone products. The successful entry into the hydrocortisone field made possible the discovery of Albamycin and the development of Medrol. Albamycin and Medrol sales underwrote the introduction of Orinase.

Like other human institutions, the pharmaceutical industry is less than perfect. There are certainly instances in the marketing of prescription drugs, both old and new, that can be complained of. Many physicians have been critical of the large number of combinations and minor variations of basic drugs on the market, of the numerous widely sold drugs that have little real therapeutic effect. Some have objected to the use of different brand names instead of a common generic name for different brands of a particular drug. And even in this era of pharmaceutical industry maturity, prescription-drug advertising addressed to physicians can sometimes seem as shrill as some ads for over-the-counter drugs.

No physician, of course, is compelled to accept any practice he finds objectionable. He need not prescribe combination drugs; he is free to use generic names in prescriptions; he can disregard advertising he dislikes. By no means all combinations or variations of previously discovered drugs, however, are useless. Many extend the field of usefulness of important medicinal agents and fulfill a need. Most of those that do not die quickly enough.

Some of these problems arise, moreover, from the nature of the pharmaceutical field as a competitive industry. During the past generation, many new firms have entered the pharmaceutical industry. Numerous identical or closely similar products are marketed by as many as several dozen firms. This has benefited the patient-consumer by providing him with multiple, competing sources of supply and speeding the introduction of new drugs. But it is hardly to be expected that no one in the pharmaceutical industry will ever press too hard, especially since aggressive selling and hard competition are the rule in most other industries. In any event, Federal laws provide a powerful means of policing the safety of drugs. And the realization of profits has financed as well as spurred the research needed to meet the desires of patients and physicians alike for improved means of treating ill-health.

The sums of money put into research and development by the pharmaceutical industry in recent years have grown almost explosively. If the industry adheres to its present practice of investing 8 to 10 per cent of its total sales in new development work, the time is near when the industry's total investment in research and development will reach a quarter of a billion dollars a year. The Upjohn Company's "plowback" into research and development has hovered between 9 and 10 per cent of sales; the Kalamazoo firm's search for new products will soon be consuming well over $15 million a year.

Sums of this size are not an extravagance. They have become a necessity for effective medical and pharmaceutical research. As with other goods and services today, the hire of scientists and laboratory assistants, the purchase of glassware, the rearing of laboratory animals have all become increasingly expensive. But this is the least cause of the rise. The major factors are more basic and even less controllable. Medical research has quite well dealt with the easy diseases. An ever larger proportion of those that remain—like cancer— are complex ailments for which remedies are unlikely to be found without a broad, many-sided research attack. Broad, many-sided research eats up manpower, facilities, money. The basic techniques and tools of research have become expensive. Medical investigators today have electron microscopes far outstripping the best optical microscopes in what they can reveal; analytical instruments able to detect and identify the merest trace of a significant substance; exquisite devices and procedures for probing every aspect of the living cell. The new tools tell the research scientists ever so much more than the old. They are indispensable—and they put the cost of a well-equipped modern laboratory into the tens or hundreds of thousands of dollars, against the few hundred dollars of the laboratories of a few decades ago.

In the course of the years, it is quite conceivable that our social and economic institutions will undergo great change. Were he to come back, a resident of the United States in 1865 would find innumerable changes, in institutions as well as gadgets, he never dreamed of. In one vital area, however, there will be no change. Progress in medicine will continue to require intensive and ever more expensive research. If the necessary money is not accumulated through the pharmaceutical industry, it will have to be provided in another way, or progress will cease.

Progress in medical research calls also for another ingredient—a sense of urgency. The Federal government and other agencies are currently spending large amounts of money on medical research. As the wartime penicillin story shows, however, it takes a sense of urgency as well as money to convert a basic discovery quickly into a useful advance.

It would be wrong to assert that medical progress would cease without a stimulus to hurry. It would not. But there would be few or no "fire-engine jobs." The pace would slacken, in an area in which speed can mean the saving of lives. In competition for markets, the pharmaceutical industry and firms like Upjohn have not only found a demonstrably efficacious means of spurring their own growth, but also of providing an ever larger array of tools for restoring and maintaining health.

Index

Accessorone, 76
Acetonyl, 60
Acti-Dione, 165–167
Adams, H. S., 100
Addison, Thomas, 129
Adrenal cortex extract (ACE), 130–
    134, 136, 137
Adrenocorticotropic hormone
    (ACTH), 136
Advertising, 27, 43, 44, 48, 228
Albamycin, 164, 167–170, 200, 220,
    233, 247, 251
Alkalizers, 56–61
    Acetonyl, 60
    Bromionyl, 60
    Citrocarbonate, 59–61, 63, 251
    Salicionyl, 60
Allen, Edgar, 111
Allen, W. Fred, 61, 234
American College of Physicians, 226
American Drug Manufacturers' As-
    sociation, 65

American Medical Association, 47, 48,
    226, 227
American Type Culture Collection,
    147
Antibiotics, 11, 13, 14, 95–97, 161–
    170, 200, 218–220, 222, 223
    Acti-Dione, 165–167
    Albamycin, 164, 167–170, 200, 220,
        233, 247, 251
    Cardelmycin, 168
    Cathomycin, 167–169
    novobiocin, 169
    Panalba, 170, 223
    Panmycin, 170
    penicillin, 95–97, 161–163, 220,
        251
    Penicillin O, 164, 165
    production methods, 218–220, 222
    streptomycin, 161, 162, 220
    tetracycline, 170
Anticoagulants, Dipaxin, 102
    heparin, 82, 101–103, 251

Antidiabetics, oral, 171–190
  carbutamide (BZ-55), 172, 174,
    190
  metahexamide, 190
  Synthalin A and B, 173
  tolbutamide (D860), 172, 174
  (*See also* Orinase)
Armour Laboratories, 136
Army-Navy "E" award, 100
Aschheim, S., 115, 116
Ascorbic acid (vitamin C), 75, 77
Aspirin, 10, 13, 17, 173
Avicenna, 218

Babcock, John C., 125
Banting, Sir Frederick Grant, 173
Barnes, Donald J., 74
Bayliss, Sir William M., 105–107
Bernard, Claude, 56, 57, 204
Berson, Solomon A., 181
Best, Charles H., 101, 173
Biological laboratory, 63
Biotin, 75
Bland-Sutton, Sir John, 68
Blaud iron pill, 27
Blood product substitutes, Gelfoam,
    99, 100, 247, 251
  Plazmoid, 99
Blood products, fibrin foam, 99, 100
  gamma globulin, 97, 99
  plasma, 97, 98
  serum albumin, 97–99
Blyth and Company, 239
Brockedon, William, 221
Bromionyl, 60
Brook Lodge, 38, 39, 241
Browne, J. S. L., 120
Brownell, Katherine A., 130
Burbidge, Earl L., 172
BZ-55 (carbutamide), 172, 174, 190

Caldwell, Eugene, 56
Cancer chemotheraphy screening pro-
    gram, 195, 198
Carbutamide (BZ-55), 172, 174, 190
Cardelmycin, 168
Caripeptic Liquid, 33, 34
Cartland, George F., 114, 116, 132

Cathomycin, 167–169
Cerelexin, 76, 77
Chain, Ernest, 95, 96, 220
Chakravorty, P. N., 121
Cheracol, 64, 223
Childs, Frederick L., 33, 34, 40
Chlorpromazine, 13
Chorionic gonadotropin, 115–117
Citrocarbonate, 59–61, 63, 251
Clinical testing, 89, 204–214
  of Orinase, 176–180
Cod liver oil, 67–74, 76, 77
Cohn, Edwin J., 97, 98, 116
Colwell, Arthur R., Sr., 176
Compressed tablet, 30, 220–222
Conn, Jerome W., 176, 185, 187
Cortical hormones (*see* Hormones and
    hormone products)
Cortisone and hydrocortisone, 14, 132–
    155
  microbiological production of, 143–
    149
  modifications of, 151–155
Cost accounting, 64, 65, 82
Council on Pharmacy and Chemistry,
    47, 48
Crockett, Lewie M., 44, 62, 82, 159
Cushing, Harvey, 108

D860 (tolbutamide), 172, 174
  (*See also* Orinase)
Dalton, Dorothy, 246
Death rates, by age groups, 4, 5
  maternal, 4
Detail men, 227–231, 233
Deutsch, Albert, 1
De Young, John, 38
Diabetes, 171–190
  classification, 175, 176, 180–182
  diagnosis, 182–184
  early, 184–187
  in pregnancy, 187–189
Dickens, Charles, 3
Diginfuse, 55
Digitalis, 10, 52–55, 251
Digitora, 52, 55, 63
Dipaxin, 102
Doisy, Edward A., 111–113

Dolger, Henry, 177, 178
Donehey, William, 44
Dowling, Harry F., 250
Dropsy, 52, 53
Dubos, René, 6
Ductless glands, 107–109, 129, 130

Eberly, Floyd A., 98
Ehrlich, Paul, 10
Employees, number of, in 1886, 28
  in 1920s, 61
  in 1960, 241, 242
Employment conditions, hiring, 89
  hours of work, 37, 84, 88, 243
  lay-offs, absence of, 88, 244, 245
  life insurance, 37, 82, 88, 244
  at Portage Road plant, 157, 158, 243
  wages and benefits, 88, 89, 243, 244
Endocrine glands, 107–109, 129, 130
Eppstein, Samuel H., 145, 147
Ergosterol, 72
Estradiol cyclopentylpropionate
  (ECP), 120
Estrogenic hormones, 111–114, 119
Evans, Herbert M., 115

Fajans, Stefan S., 185, 187
Farbwerke Hoechst, 172, 174
Fevig, Glenn E., 124
Fibrin foam, 99, 100
Finland, Maxwell, 167
Fleming, Sir Alexander, 95, 220
Florey, Sir Howard W., 95, 96, 220
Folkers, Karl, 78
Food and Drug Administration, 69,
  70, 175, 199, 206, 207, 209–211
Food, Drug and Cosmetic Act of 1938,
  175, 209, 210, 233
Ford, Henry, 237
Ford Foundation, 240
Ford Motor Company, 237, 240
Fortune, 15
Foxglove (*see* Digitalis)
Friable pills, 25–28, 221, 251
Fuchs, J., 173, 174

Galbraith, Malcolm, 65, 87, 88, 93
Gamma globulin, 97, 99

Gelatin capsule, 220
Gelfoam, 99, 100, 247, 251
Gilmore, Donald Sherwood, 83, 84,
  138, 159, 160, 236, 246
Gilmore, Genevieve Upjohn, 83, 246
Gilmore, James F., 36, 83
Gilmore, John M., 29, 83
Goldberger, Joseph, 75
Gonadogen, 116, 117
"Grand Rounds," 228
Greiner, J. Ward, 124

Hailman, Harold F., 206
Haines, W. J., 144
Halotestin, 126, 127
Harrop, Leslie D., 93, 94, 209
Hart, Merrill C., 51, 138, 139
Hartman, Frank A., 130
Hartman, Homer J., 167
Hartroft, W. Stanley, 181
Heidelberger, Michael, 142
Heinle, Robert W., 202
Hench, Philip S., 134–137
Heparin, 82, 101–103, 251
Herr, Milton E., 123, 149
Heyl, Frederick William, 34, 51–55,
  58, 59, 70, 89, 90, 102, 121, 123,
  138, 149, 191, 192, 223
Hippocrates, 205
Hoet, J. P., 189
Hogg, John A., 148
Holbrook, Stewart H., 23
Hormones, general discussion, 10, 11,
  13, 104–110
  steroid, 109–111
Hormones and hormone products,
  adrenal cortex extract (ACE),
    130–134, 136, 137
  adrenocorticotropic hormone
    (ACTH), 136
  chorionic gonadotropin, 115–117
  cortisone and hydrocortisone, 14,
    132–155
  microbiological production of,
    143–149
  modifications of, 151–155
  estradiol cyclopentylpropionate
    (ECP), 120

Hormones and hormone products,
  estrogenic, 111–114, 119
  Gonadogen, 116, 117
  Halotestin, 126, 127
  insulin, 10, 171, 173–176, 178–182,
    185, 190
  Lipo-Adrenal Extract, 136, 137
  Medrol, 125, 148, 153, 154, 208, 216,
    247, 251
  methyltestosterone, 126
  Oxylone, 154, 155
  Prodox, 124, 125
  progesterone, 118, 120–126, 147–149
  Provera, 125, 126, 233
  testosterone, 119
  testosterone cyclopentylpropionate
    (TCP), 120
  Urestrin, 114, 117
Howell, William Henry, 101
Hume, E. M., 71
Hydrocortisone (*see* Cortisone and
  hydrocortisone)
Hynson, Westcott & Dunning, 94
Hypoglycemic agents, oral, 171–190
  carbutamide (BZ-55), 172, 174,
    190
  metahexamide, 190
  Synthalin A and B, 173
  tolbutamide (D860), 172, 174
  (*See also* Orinase)

Influenza, 5
Ingle, Dwight, 132, 149
Insulin, 10, 171, 173–176, 178–182,
  185, 190
International Vitamin Corporation,
  73

Jackson, W. P. U., 188, 189
Jacobs, Walter A., 142
Janbon, M., 173
Jeculin, 77
Jenner, Edward, 2
Jones, Henry D., 29
*Journal of the American Medical
  Association,* 48

Kalamazoo Foundation, 38, 245

Kazoo Mints, 50
Kendall, E. C., 132
Koch, Fred C., 145
Koch, Robert, 2
Kuizenga, Marvin H., 102, 119, 130–
  132, 136, 144

Lacy, Paul E., 181
Laënnec, René, 2
Laxative (*see* Phenolax; Pills, Anti-
  Constipation, Upjohn)
Lederle Laboratories, 16
Levin, Robert H., 121, 152
Levine, Rachmiel, 176
Life expectancy, 3
Light, Richard Upjohn, 246
Light, S. Rudolph, 51, 56
Light, Winifred Upjohn, 51, 236, 246
Lilly, Eli, & Co., 164, 190
Lipo-Adrenal Extract, 136, 137
Lipomul i.v., 215
Little, William F., 51
Loubatières, Auguste, 173
Lukens, F. D., 189

McClelland, George C., 47
McCollum, E. V., 69, 71
McLean, Jay, 101
Madison, Leonard L., 182, 183
Marble, Alexander, 177
Market analysis, 47, 81
Marketing, 231–234
Medical advance, 1–10
Medical division, 89, 101, 205, 206, 211
Medical education, continuing educa-
  tion of physicians in practice,
    225–227
  AMA survey, 226, 227
Medrol, 125, 148, 153, 154, 208, 216,
    247, 251
Medule, 216, 222
Mellanby, Sir Edward, 69
Merck & Co., Inc., 15, 133–135, 139,
  141, 149, 167–169, 210
Metahexamide, 190
Methyltestosterone, 126
Miller, H. C., 189
Mirsky, I. Arthur, 176, 183

Morgan Stanley & Co., 240
Moseley, Virginia Conner, 160
Mothe, Monsieur de, 220
Murray, Herbert C., 145–147
Myeladol, 76
Mylax, 92

Naming of drugs, 232, 233
National Formulary, 221
New Drug Application, 199, 206, 209, 210
New York Stock Exchange, 240
Niacinamide, 75, 77
Nitroglycerine, 50, 52
Norton, John F., 94
Novobiocin, 169
Nutrition laboratory, 70, 71, 73, 76–78

O'Donovan, C. J., 177
Origins of drugs, 9–14
    table, 12
Orinase, 13, 172, 174–187, 189, 190, 208, 232, 233, 247, 251
    clinical trial of, 176–180
    in diagnosis, 182–184
    in early diabetes, 184–189
Ott, Arnold C., 119
The Overflow, 35, 81, 82
Oxylone, 154, 155

Palmo-Dionin, 33
Panalba, 170, 223
Panmycin, 170
Pantothenic acid, 75, 78
Pasteur, Louis, 2
Patent medicines, 17, 23, 49
Patterson, C. V., 61, 100, 101
Pavlov, Ivan P., 106
Penicillin, 95–97, 161–163, 220, 251
Penicillin O, 164, 165
Penick, S. B., & Co., 142
Personnel department, 89, 243–245
Peterson, Durey H., 145–147, 149, 152
Pfiffner, Joseph J., 130
Pfizer, Chas., & Co., 15, 168
Pharmaceutical elegance, 218
Pharmaceutical engineering, 215–224

Pharmaceutical industry, 11–21, 43, 160, 161, 227, 250–254
    research, 11–14, 20, 160, 161, 252–254
    sales promotion, 17, 43, 227
Phenolax, 40–45, 59, 63, 92, 251
Phenolphthalein, 40–43
Pill Cactus Compound, 33
Pill Methylene Blue Compound, 33
Pills, Anti-Constipation, Upjohn, 27, 41
Plasma, 97, 98
Plazmoid, 99
Pollock, Montague, 56, 58
Portage Road plant, 154–160, 236, 241–243
Prodox, 124, 125
Progesterone, 118, 120–126, 147–149
Provera, 125, 126, 233
Public health, 2–8
Public Health Service, U.S., 75, 209
Pure Food and Drug Act, 49, 50
Pyocyanase, 10
Pyridoxine (vitamin B_6), 75, 77

Quinine, 27

Rastinon, 172
Reichstein, Tadeusz, 132, 142
Reilly, H. Christine, 166
Remington's Practice of Pharmacy, 221
Research, pharmaceutical industry, 11–14, 20, 160, 161
    financing of, 252–254
    Upjohn, on antibiotics, 163–170
        on anticoagulants, 101–103
        beginning of, 49–51
        on blood product substitutes, 99, 100
        on cortical hormones, 129–155
        on digitalis, 52–55
        on Orinase, 171–190
        on production methods, 218–224
        on sex hormones, 111–127
        on vitamins, 67–79
    (*See also* Clinical testing)

Research laboratories, 62, 63, 89–91, 191–203, 242
Research fellowships, Upjohn, 89, 90, 102
Research screening, 197–200
Research Tower, 62, 91
Riboflavin (vitamin B₂), 75, 77
Richland Farms, 85, 86, 114, 241
Rickets, 68, 69, 71, 72
Rogoff, J. M., 130

Sales, overseas, 92, 93, 248
Sales organization, 45–48, 65, 66, 87, 88, 225–234
Sales promotion, 227, 228
Sales volume, in 1886, 28, 29
  in 1890, 30
  in 1920s, 61
  in 1930s, 87
  in 1945, 79, 100
  in 1959, 240
  growth in, 246
  overseas, 248
Salesmen, detail men, 227–231, 233
  first, 45
  number of, in 1925, 65
  salaried, 46, 229
Salicionyl, 60
Salvarsan and neosalvarsan, 10
Sasaki, landscape architect, 160
Savage, George M., 168
Schering Corporation, 152
Schreiber, Richard S., 138, 139, 192, 202, 203
Scope Weekly, 228
Sellman, Richard, 239
Sellman, Waters H., 46, 239
Serum albumin, 97–99
Sex hormones (*see* Hormones and hormone products)
Sherman, Harry C., 75
Sherry, Sol, 177
Skidmore, Owings and Merrill, 159, 160
Solu-B, 78
Squibb, E. R., and Son, 16, 151
Staley, J. Fred, 51, 52
Stare, Frederick J., 215, 216

Starling, Ernest Henry, 105–107
Steenbock, Harry, 72
Steenbock irradiation process, 71, 72, 74
Steroid hormones, 109–111
  (*See also* Hormones and hormone products)
Stewart, G. N., 130
Stock, C. Chester, 166
Streptomycin, 161, 162, 220
Strophanthus vine, 140–143
Sulfadiazine, 94
Sulfanilamide, 10, 11, 13, 93, 94
Super D cod liver oil, 71–74, 251
Suter, Loyal S., 170
Swingle, W. W., 130
Sydney Ross Company, 31
Synthalin A and B, 173

Teleostol Compound C, 77
Testosterone, 119
  (*See also* Methyltestosterone)
Testosterone cyclopentylpropionate (TCP), 120
Tetracycline, 170
Thiamine (vitamin B₁), 75, 77
Thumb trademark, 27, 28
Tolbutamide (D860), 172, 174
  (*See also* Orinase)
Tonics, 69, 70
Turbeville, H. E., 243

Ulrich, Elizabeth W., 170
Unger, Roger H., 182, 183
Unicap, 74, 77, 78, 251
Unicap M, 78
Unicap Therapeutic, 78
United States Pharmacopoeia, 10, 11, 23
University of Michigan, 24
Upjohn, Carrie Gilmore, 36, 83
Upjohn, Everett Gifford, 84, 85, 89, 101, 112, 113, 130, 159
Upjohn, Frederick L., 26, 28, 29, 31, 46, 48
Upjohn, Grace, 246
Upjohn, Helen, 24
Upjohn, Henry U., 24–26, 28, 29

Upjohn, James T., 25, 26, 28, 29, 41,
  48, 51
Upjohn, Lawrence N., 35, 40, 46, 47,
  56, 58, 59, 83–85, 159
Upjohn, Millie Kirby, 25, 29
Upjohn, Rachel Babcock, 36
Upjohn, Uriah, 24
Upjohn, W. E., Institute, 86
Upjohn, William Erastus, 16, 40–42,
  46–52, 58, 62, 64, 65, 89, 154, 235,
  245, 246
  death, 86, 87
  founding of company, 24, 29
  sketch, 34–39
  successors of, 80–85
  unemployment project, 85, 86
Upjohn, William Harold, 35, 37, 47,
  62, 81, 82, 87, 101, 236
Upjohn Company stock, ownership
  of, 29, 48, 80, 81, 235–240
  price of, 237–239
  public sale of, 238–240
Upjohn philanthropies in Kalamazoo,
  245, 246
Upjohn Pill and Granule Company,
  22–32
Upjohn-Richland Farms, 85, 86, 114,
  241
Upjohn trademark, 27, 28
Urestrin, 114, 117

Vaccines, 63
Varney, Franklin G., 89
Venning, Eleanor, 120
Vitamin preparations, Accessorone, 76
  Cerelexin, 76, 77
  Jeculin, 77
  Myeladol, 76
  Solu-B, 78
  Super D cod liver oil, 71–74, 251

Vitamin preparations,
  Teleostol Compound C, 77
  Unicap, 74, 77, 78, 251
  Unicap M, 78
  Unicap Therapeutic, 78
  Vitrate, 76
  Zymacap, 78
  Zymadrops, 78
Vitamins, 13–15, 17, 67–78
  A, 69–74, 76, 77
  B complex, 69, 74–78
  B$_1$ (thiamine), 75, 77
  B$_2$ (riboflavin), 75, 77
  B$_6$ (pyridoxine), 75, 77
  B$_{12}$, 78
  biotin, 75
  C (ascorbic acid), 75, 77
  D, 67–74, 76, 77
  D$_2$, 74
  D$_3$, 74
  niacinamide, 75, 77
  pantothenic acid, 75, 78
Vitrate, 76

War production, 93–101
Weisblat, David I., 138, 202
Welch, Henry, 167
Whiffen, Alma J., 165, 167
White Office, 51, 52, 62, 82, 90, 91,
  154
Wilkerson, Hugh, 189
Williams, Robert R., 75
Williams, Roger J., 75
Wise, Edwin C., 70–73, 76
Withering, William, 52
Woolf, N., 188
Wright, Frank Lloyd, 241

Zondek, Bernhard, 115, 116
Zymacap, 78
Zymadrops, 78